Updated Indiana Academic Standards for English/Language Arts Grade 2

P9-DHG-582

Unit 1 • Iris and Walter

Day One

Pages 1–2 • Family Times

RD.2.2.5 Restate facts and details or summarize the main idea in the text to clarify and organize ideas.

LS.2.7.6 Speak clearly and at an appropriate pace for the type of communication (such as an informal discussion or a report to class).

LS.2.7.8 Retell stories, including characters, setting, and plot.

Page 3 • Short Vowels

RD.2.1.1 Demonstrate an awareness of the sounds that are made by different letters by: distinguishing beginning, middle, and ending sounds in words; rhyming words; clearly pronouncing blends and vowel sounds.

RD.2.1.3 Decode (sound out) regular words with more than one syllable (*dinosaur, vacation*).

WR.2.6.9 Spell correctly words with short- and long-vowel sounds (*a, e, i, o, u*), r-controlled vowels (*ar, er, ir, or, ur*), and consonant-blend patterns (*bl, dr, st*).

Page 4 • Character and Setting

RD.2.3.1 Compare plots, settings, and characters presented by different authors.

LS.2.7.8 Retell stories, including characters, setting, and plot.

LS.2.7.10 Recount experiences or present stories that: move through a logical sequence of events; describe story elements, including characters, plot, and setting.

Day Two

Page 5 • Character and Setting

RD.2.3.1 Compare plots, settings, and characters presented by different authors.

LS.2.7.8 Retell stories, including characters, setting, and plot.

LS.2.7.10 Recount experiences or present stories that: move through a logical sequence of events; describe story elements, including characters, plot, and setting.

Page 6 • High-Frequency and Selection Words

RD.2.1.2 Recognize and use knowledge of spelling patterns (such as *cut/cutting, slide/sliding*) when reading.

RD.2.1.3 Decode (sound out) regular words with more than one syllable (*dinosaur, vacation*).

RD.2.1.5 Identify and correctly use regular plural words (*mountain/mountains*) and irregular plural words (*child/children, mouse/mice*).

Page 7 • Main Idea and Details

RD.2.2.5 Restate facts and details or summarize the main idea in the text to clarify and organize ideas.

LS.2.7.2 Ask for clarification and explanation of stories and ideas.

LS.2.7.3 Paraphrase (restate in own words) information that has been shared orally by others.

Day Three

Page 8 • Syllable Pattern VC/CV and VCC/V

RD.2.1.1 Demonstrate an awareness of the sounds that are made by different letters by: distinguishing beginning, middle, and ending sounds in words; rhyming words; clearly pronouncing blends and vowel sounds.

RD.2.1.2 Recognize and use knowledge of spelling patterns (such as *cut/cutting, slide/sliding*) when reading.

RD.2.1.3 Decode (sound out) regular words with more than one syllable (*dinosaur, vacation*).

Page 9 • High-Frequency Words

RD.2.1.3 Decode (sound out) regular words with more than one syllable (*dinosaur, vacation*).

RD.2.1.5 Identify and correctly use regular plural words (*mountain/mountains*) and irregular plural words (*child/children, mouse/mice*).

RD.2.1.6 Read aloud fluently and accurately with appropriate changes in voice and expression.

Day Five

Page 10 • Media Center/Library

WR.2.4.3 Find ideas for writing stories and descriptions in pictures or books.

LS.2.7.11 Report on a topic with facts and details, drawing from several sources of information.

Unit 1 • Exploring Space with an Astronaut

Day One

Pages 11–12 • Family Times

LS.2.7.6 Speak clearly and at an appropriate pace for the type of communication (such as an informal discussion or a report to class).

LS.2.7.10 Recount experiences or present stories that: move through a logical sequence of events; describe story elements, including characters, plot, and setting.

Page 13 • Long Vowels CVCe

RD.2.1.1 Demonstrate an awareness of the sounds that are made by different letters by: distinguishing beginning, middle, and ending sounds in words; rhyming words; clearly pronouncing blends and vowel sounds.

RD.2.1.2 Recognize and use knowledge of spelling patterns (such as *cut/cutting, slide/sliding*) when reading.

WR.2.6.9 Spell correctly words with short- and long-vowel sounds (*a, e, i, o, u*), r-controlled vowels (*ar, er, ir, or, ur*), and consonant-blend patterns (*bl, dr, st*).

Page 14 • Main Idea and Details

RD.2.2.5 Restate facts and details or summarize the main idea in the text to clarify and organize ideas.

LS.2.7.2 Ask for clarification and explanation of stories and ideas.

LS.2.7.3 Paraphrase (restate in own words) information that has been shared orally by others.

Day Two

Page 15 • Main Idea and Details

RD.2.2.5 Restate facts and details or summarize the main idea in the text to clarify and organize ideas.

LS.2.7.2 Ask for clarification and explanation of stories and ideas.

LS.2.7.3 Paraphrase (restate in own words) information that has been shared orally by others.

Page 16 • High-Frequency and Selection Words

RD.2.1.5 Identify and correctly use regular plural words (*mountain/mountains*) and irregular plural words (*child/children, mouse/mice*).

RD.2.1.6 Read aloud fluently and accurately with appropriate changes in voice and expression.

RD.2.1.7 Understand and explain common synonyms (words with the same meaning) and antonyms (words with opposite meanings).

Page 17 • Author's Purpose

RD.2.2.3 Use knowledge of the author's purpose(s) to comprehend informational text.

RD.2.3.4.3 Understand or interpret what is read or heard by responding to questions (*who, what, when, where, why, how*) and by using appropriate comprehension strategies, such as drawing conclusions, identifying the author's purpose, relating to prior knowledge, restating details, or setting a purpose for reading.

Day Three

Page 18 • Short Vowels

RD.2.1.1 Demonstrate an awareness of the sounds that are made by different letters by: distinguishing beginning, middle, and ending sounds in words; rhyming words; clearly pronouncing blends and vowel sounds.

RD.2.1.3 Decode (sound out) regular words with more than one syllable (*dinosaur, vacation*).

WR.2.6.9 Spell correctly words with short- and long-vowel sounds (*a, e, i, o, u*), r-controlled vowels (*ar, er, ir, or, ur*), and consonant-blend patterns (*bl, dr, st*).

Page 19 • High-Frequency Words

RD.2.1.7 Understand and explain common synonyms (words with the same meaning) and antonyms (words with opposite meanings).

RD.2.1.8 Use knowledge of individual words to predict the meaning of unknown compound words (*lunchtime, lunchroom, daydream, raindrop*).

WR.2.6.8 Spell correctly words like *was, were, says, said, who, what,* and *why,* which are used frequently but do not fit common spelling patterns.

Day Five

Page 20 • Alphabetical Order

WR.2.4.4 Understand the purposes of various reference materials (such as a dictionary, thesaurus, or atlas).

WR.2.6.1 Form letters correctly and space words and sentences properly so that writing can be read easily by another person.

Unit 1 • Henry and Mudge and the Starry Night

Day One

Pages 21–22 • Family Times

RD.2.1.6 Read aloud fluently and accurately with appropriate changes in voice and expression.

LS.2.7.7 Tell experiences in a logical order.

LS.2.7.9 Report on a topic with supportive facts and details.

Page 23 • Consonant Blends

RD.2.1.1 Demonstrate an awareness of the sounds that are made by different letters by: distinguishing beginning, middle, and ending sounds in words; rhyming words; clearly pronouncing blends and vowel sounds.

RD.2.1.3 Decode (sound out) regular words with more than one syllable (*dinosaur, vacation*).

WR.2.6.9 Spell correctly words with short- and long-vowel sounds (*a, e, i, o, u*), r-controlled vowels (*ar, er, ir, or, ur*), and consonant-blend patterns (*bl, dr, st*).

Page 24 • Character and Setting

RD.2.3.1 Compare plots, settings, and characters presented by different authors.

LS.2.7.8 Retell stories, including characters, setting, and plot.

LS.2.7.10 Recount experiences or present stories that: move through a logical sequence of events; describe story elements, including characters, plot, and setting.

Day Two

Page 25 • Character and Setting

RD.2.3.1 Compare plots, settings, and characters presented by different authors.

LS.2.7.8 Retell stories, including characters, setting, and plot.

LS.2.7.10 Recount experiences or present stories that: move through a logical sequence of events; describe story elements, including characters, plot, and setting.

Page 26 • High-Frequency and Selection Words

RD.2.1.8 Use knowledge of individual words to predict the meaning of unknown compound words (*lunchtime, lunchroom, daydream, raindrop*).

RD.2.1.10 Identify simple multiple-meaning words (*change, duck*).

WR.2.4.4 Understand the purposes of various reference materials (such as a dictionary, thesaurus, or atlas).

Page 27 • Realism and Fantasy

RD.2.2.2 State the purpose for reading.

RD.2.3.4.1 Recognize the difference between fantasy and reality.

Day Three

Page 28 • Long Vowels CVCe

RD.2.1.1 Demonstrate an awareness of the sounds that are made by different letters by: distinguishing beginning, middle, and ending sounds in words; rhyming words; clearly pronouncing blends and vowel sounds.

WR.2.6.9 Spell correctly words with short- and long-vowel sounds (*a, e, i, o, u*), r-controlled vowels (*ar, er, ir, or, ur*), and consonant-blend patterns (*bl, dr, st*).

Page 29 • High-Frequency Words

RD.2.1.8 Use knowledge of individual words to predict the meaning of unknown compound words (*lunchtime, lunchroom, daydream, raindrop*).

RD.2.1.10 Identify simple multiple-meaning words (*change, duck*).

WR.2.6.8 Spell correctly words like *was, were, says, said, who, what,* and *why,* which are used frequently but do not fit common spelling patterns.

Day Five

Page 30 • Parts of a Book

RD.2.2.1 Use titles, tables of contents, and chapter headings to locate information in text.

WR.2.4.4 Understand the purposes of various reference materials (such as a dictionary, thesaurus, or atlas).

Unit 1 • A Walk in the Desert

Day One

Pages 31–32 • Family Times

RD.2.1.6 Read aloud fluently and accurately with appropriate changes in voice and expression.

RD.2.2.5 Restate facts and details or summarize the main idea in the text to clarify and organize ideas.

LS.2.7.9 Report on a topic with supportive facts and details.

Page 33 • Base Words and Endings

RD.2.1.2 Recognize and use knowledge of spelling patterns (such as *cut/cutting, slide/sliding*) when reading.

RD.2.1.5 Identify and correctly use regular plural words (*mountain/mountains*) and irregular plural words (*child/children, mouse/mice*).

RD.2.1.8.1 Read and understand more difficult root words (such as *chase*) and their inflectional forms (*chases, chased, chasing*).

Page 34 • Main Idea and Details

RD.2.2.3 Use knowledge of the author's purpose(s) to comprehend informational text.

RD.2.2.4 Ask and respond to questions (*why, what if, how*) to aid comprehension about important elements of informational texts.

RD.2.2.5 Restate facts and details or summarize the main idea in the text to clarify and organize ideas.

Day Two

Page 35 • Main Idea and Details

RD.2.2.3 Use knowledge of the author's purpose(s) to comprehend informational text.

RD.2.2.5 Restate facts and details or summarize the main idea in the text to clarify and organize ideas.

LS.2.7.9 Report on a topic with supportive facts and details.

Page 36 • High-Frequency Words

RD.2.1.2 Recognize and use knowledge of spelling patterns (such as *cut/cutting, slide/sliding*) when reading.

RD.2.1.10 Identify simple multiple-meaning words (*change, duck*).

WR.2.6.8 Spell correctly words like *was, were, says, said, who, what,* and *why,* which are used frequently but do not fit common spelling patterns.

Page 37 • Compare and Contrast

RD.2.2.3 Use knowledge of the author's purpose(s) to comprehend informational text.

RD.2.2.4 Ask and respond to questions (*why, what if, how*) to aid comprehension about important elements of informational texts.

RD.2.2.5 Restate facts and details or summarize the main idea in the text to clarify and organize ideas.

Day Three

Page 38 • Consonant Blends

RD.2.1.1 Demonstrate an awareness of the sounds that are made by different letters by: distinguishing beginning, middle, and ending sounds in words; rhyming words; clearly pronouncing blends and vowel sounds.

RD.2.1.3 Decode (sound out) regular words with more than one syllable (*dinosaur, vacation*).

WR.2.6.9 Spell correctly words with short- and long-vowel sounds (*a, e, i, o, u*), *r*-controlled vowels (*ar, er, ir, or, ur*), and consonant-blend patterns (*bl, dr, st*).

Page 39 • High-Frequency Words

RD.2.1.2 Recognize and use knowledge of spelling patterns (such as *cut/cutting, slide/sliding*) when reading.

RD.2.1.3 Decode (sound out) regular words with more than one syllable (*dinosaur, vacation*).

RD.2.1.5 Identify and correctly use regular plural words (*mountain/mountains*) and irregular plural words (*child/children, mouse/mice*).

Day Five

Page 40 • Online Reference Sources

WR.2.4.4 Understand the purposes of various reference materials (such as a dictionary, thesaurus, or atlas).

WR.2.4.5 Use a computer to draft, revise, and publish writing.

Unit 1 • The Strongest One

Day One

Pages 41–42 • Family Times

RD.2.2.6 Recognize cause-and-effect relationships in a text.

RD.2.3.1 Compare plots, settings, and characters presented by different authors.

LS.2.7.6 Speak clearly and at an appropriate pace for the type of communication (such as an informal discussion or a report to class).

Page 43 • Consonant Digraphs

RD.2.1.1 Demonstrate an awareness of the sounds that are made by different letters by: distinguishing beginning, middle, and ending sounds in words; rhyming words; clearly pronouncing blends and vowel sounds.

WR.2.6.9 Spell correctly words with short- and long-vowel sounds (*a, e, i, o, u*), *r*-controlled vowels (*ar, er, ir, or, ur*), and consonant-blend patterns (*bl, dr, st*).

Page 44 • Realism and Fantasy

RD.2.2.2 State the purpose for reading.

RD.2.3.4.1 Recognize the difference between fantasy and reality.

Day Two

Page 45 • Realism and Fantasy

RD.2.2.2 State the purpose for reading.

RD.2.3.4.1 Recognize the difference between fantasy and reality.

Page 46 • High-Frequency and Selection Words

RD.2.1.3 Decode (sound out) regular words with more than one syllable (*dinosaur, vacation*).

RD.2.1.5 Identify and correctly use regular plural words (*mountain/mountains*) and irregular plural words (*child/children, mouse/mice*).

RD.2.1.7 Understand and explain common synonyms (words with the same meaning) and antonyms (words with opposite meanings).

Page 47 • Character and Setting

RD.2.3.1 Compare plots, settings, and characters presented by different authors.

LS.2.7.8 Retell stories, including characters, setting, and plot.

LS.2.7.10 Recount experiences or present stories that: move through a logical sequence of events; describe story elements, including characters, plot, and setting.

Day Three

Page 48 • Inflected Endings

RD.2.1.2 Recognize and use knowledge of spelling patterns (such as *cut/cutting, slide/sliding*) when reading.

RD.2.1.8.1 Read and understand more difficult root words (such as *chase*) and their inflectional forms (*chases, chased, chasing*).

Page 49 • High-Frequency Words

RD.2.1.2 Recognize and use knowledge of spelling patterns (such as *cut/cutting, slide/sliding*) when reading.

RD.2.1.5 Identify and correctly use regular plural words (*mountain/mountains*) and irregular plural words (*child/children, mouse/mice*).

RD.2.1.6 Read aloud fluently and accurately with appropriate changes in voice and expression.

Day Five

Page 50 • Maps

RD.2.2.7 Interpret information from diagrams, charts, and graphs.

WR.2.4.4 Understand the purposes of various reference materials (such as a dictionary, thesaurus, or atlas).

Unit 2 • Tara and Tiree, Fearless Friends

Day One

Pages 51–52 • Family Times

RD.2.2.6 Recognize cause-and-effect relationships in a text.

LS.2.7.6 Speak clearly and at an appropriate pace for the type of communication (such as an informal discussion or a report to class).

LS.2.7.7 Tell experiences in a logical order.

Page 53 • *r*-Controlled *ar, or, ore*

RD.2.1.1 Demonstrate an awareness of the sounds that are made by different letters by: distinguishing beginning, middle, and ending sounds in words; rhyming words; clearly pronouncing blends and vowel sounds.

RD.2.1.3 Decode (sound out) regular words with more than one syllable (*dinosaur, vacation*).

WR.2.6.9 Spell correctly words with short- and long-vowel sounds (*a, e, i, o, u*), *r*-controlled vowels (*ar, er, ir, or, ur*), and consonant-blend patterns (*bl, dr, st*).

Page 54 • Sequence

RD.2.2.1.1 Identify text that uses sequence or other logical order (alphabetical order, time).

LS.2.7.7 Tell experiences in a logical order.

LS.2.7.10 Recount experiences or present stories that: move through a logical sequence of events; describe story elements, including characters, plot, and setting.

Day Two

Page 55 • Sequence

RD.2.2.1.1 Identify text that uses sequence or other logical order (alphabetical order, time).

LS.2.7.7 Tell experiences in a logical order.

LS.2.7.10 Recount experiences or present stories that: move through a logical sequence of events; describe story elements, including characters, plot, and setting.

Page 56 • High-Frequency and Selection Words

RD.2.1.5 Identify and correctly use regular plural words (*mountain/mountains*) and irregular plural words (*child/children, mouse/mice*).

RD.2.1.6 Read aloud fluently and accurately with appropriate changes in voice and expression.

RD.2.1.7 Understand and explain common synonyms (words with the same meaning) and antonyms (words with opposite meanings).

Page 57 • Character and Setting

RD.2.3.1 Compare plots, settings, and characters presented by different authors.

LS.2.7.8 Retell stories, including characters, setting, and plot.

LS.2.7.10 Recount experiences or present stories that: move through a logical sequence of events; describe story elements, including characters, plot, and setting.

Day Three

Page 58 • Consonant Digraphs

RD.2.1.1 Demonstrate an awareness of the sounds that are made by different letters by: distinguishing beginning, middle, and ending sounds in words; rhyming words; clearly pronouncing blends and vowel sounds.

WR.2.6.9 Spell correctly words with short- and long-vowel sounds (*a, e, i, o, u*), *r*-controlled vowels (*ar, er, ir, or, ur*), and consonant-blend patterns (*bl, dr, st*).

Page 59 • High-Frequency Words

RD.2.1.8 Use knowledge of individual words to predict the meaning of unknown compound words (*lunchtime, lunchroom, daydream, raindrop*).

RD.2.1.10 Identify simple multiple-meaning words (*change, duck*).

WR.2.4.4 Understand the purposes of various reference materials (such as a dictionary, thesaurus, or atlas).

Day Five

Page 60 • Glossary

WR.2.4.4 Understand the purposes of various reference materials (such as a dictionary, thesaurus, or atlas).

LS.2.7.11 Report on a topic with facts and details, drawing from several sources of information.

Unit 2 • Ronald Morgan Goes to Bat

Day One

Pages 61–62 • Family Times

RD.2.1.6 Read aloud fluently and accurately with appropriate changes in voice and expression.

RD.2.3.2 Create different endings to stories (predictions) and identify the reason (problem) and the impact of the different ending (solution).

LS.2.7.8 Retell stories, including characters, setting, and plot.

Page 63 • Contractions

RD.2.1.2 Recognize and use knowledge of spelling patterns (such as *cut/cutting, slide/sliding*) when reading.

RD.2.1.3 Decode (sound out) regular words with more than one syllable (*dinosaur, vacation*).

WR.2.6.8 Spell correctly words like *was*, *were*, *says*, *said*, *who*, *what*, and *why*, which are used frequently but do not fit common spelling patterns.

Page 64 • Realism and Fantasy

RD.2.2.2 State the purpose for reading.

RD.2.3.4.1 Recognize the difference between fantasy and reality.

Day Two

Page 65 • Realism and Fantasy

RD.2.2.2 State the purpose for reading.

RD.2.3.4.1 Recognize the difference between fantasy and reality.

Page 66 • High-Frequency and Selection Words

RD.2.1.2 Recognize and use knowledge of spelling patterns (such as *cut/cutting, slide/sliding*) when reading.

RD.2.1.10 Identify simple multiple-meaning words (*change, duck*).

WR.2.4.4 Understand the purposes of various reference materials (such as a dictionary, thesaurus, atlas).

Page 67 • Sequence

RD.2.2.1.1 Identify text that uses sequence or other logical order (alphabetical order, time).

LS.2.7.7 Tell experiences in a logical order.

LS.2.7.10 Recount experiences or present stories that: move through a logical sequence of events; describe story elements, including characters, plot, and setting.

Day Three

Page 68 • *r*-Controlled

RD.2.1.1 Demonstrate an awareness of the sounds that are made by different letters by: distinguishing beginning, middle, and ending sounds in words; rhyming words; clearly pronouncing blends and vowel sounds.

WR.2.6.9 Spell correctly words with short- and long-vowel sounds (*a, e, i, o, u*), *r*-controlled vowels (*ar, er, ir, or, ur*), and consonant-blend patterns (*bl, dr, st*).

Page 69 • High-Frequency Words

RD.2.1.3 Decode (sound out) regular words with more than one syllable (*dinosaur, vacation*).

RD.2.1.10 Identify simple multiple-meaning words (*change, duck*).

WR.2.6.8 Spell correctly words like *was*, *were*, *says*, *said*, *who*, *what*, and *why*, which are used frequently but do not fit common spelling patterns.

Day Five

Page 70 • Newspapers and Periodicals

WR.2.4.4 Understand the purposes of various reference materials (such as a dictionary, thesaurus, or atlas).

LS.2.7.11 Report on a topic with facts and details, drawing from several sources of information.

Unit 2 • Turtle's Race with Beaver

Day One

Pages 71–72 • Family Times

RD.2.1.6 Read aloud fluently and accurately with appropriate changes in voice and expression.

RD.2.3.1 Compare plots, settings, and characters presented by different authors.

RD.2.3.2 Create different endings to stories (predictions) and identify the reason (problem) and the impact of the different ending (solution).

Page 73 • *r*-Controlled *er, ir, ur*

RD.2.1.1 Demonstrate an awareness of the sounds that are made by different letters by: distinguishing beginning, middle, and ending sounds in words; rhyming words; clearly pronouncing blends and vowel sounds.

RD.2.1.3 Decode (sound out) regular words with more than one syllable (*dinosaur, vacation*).

WR.2.6.9 Spell correctly words with short- and long-vowel sounds (*a, e, i, o, u*), *r*-controlled vowels (*ar, er, ir, or, ur*), and consonant-blend patterns (*bl, dr, st*).

Page 74 • Sequence

RD.2.2.1.1 Identify text that uses sequence or other logical order (alphabetical order, time).

LS.2.7.7 Tell experiences in a logical order.

LS.2.7.10 Recount experiences or present stories that: move through a logical sequence of events; describe story elements, including characters, plot, and setting.

Day Two

Page 75 • Sequence

RD.2.2.1.1 Identify text that uses sequence or other logical order (alphabetical order, time).

LS.2.7.7 Tell experiences in a logical order.

LS.2.7.10 Recount experiences or present stories that: move through a logical sequence of events; describe story elements, including characters, plot, and setting.

Page 76 • High-Frequency and Selection Words

RD.2.1.2 Recognize and use knowledge of spelling patterns (such as *cut/cutting, slide/sliding*) when reading.

RD.2.1.3 Decode (sound out) regular words with more than one syllable (*dinosaur, vacation*).

WR.2.4.4 Understand the purposes of various reference materials (such as a dictionary, thesaurus, or atlas).

Page 77 • Realism and Fantasy

RD.2.2.2 State the purpose for reading.

RD.2.3.4.1 Recognize the difference between fantasy and reality.

Day Three

Page 78 • Contractions

RD.2.1.2 Recognize and use knowledge of spelling patterns (such as *cut/cutting, slide/sliding*) when reading.

RD.2.1.3 Decode (sound out) regular words with more than one syllable (*dinosaur, vacation*).

WR.2.6.8 Spell correctly words like *was, were, says, said, who, what,* and *why,* which are used frequently but do not fit common spelling patterns.

Page 79 • High-Frequency Words

RD.2.1.3 Decode (sound out) regular words with more than one syllable (*dinosaur, vacation*).

RD.2.1.6 Read aloud fluently and accurately with appropriate changes in voice and expression.

WR.2.6.8 Spell correctly words like *was, were, says, said, who, what,* and *why,* which are used frequently but do not fit common spelling patterns.

Day Five

Page 80 • Use a Dictionary

WR.2.4.4 Understand the purposes of various reference materials (such as a dictionary, thesaurus, or atlas).

LS.2.7.11 Report on a topic with facts and details, drawing from several sources of information.

Unit 2 • The Bremen Town Musicians

Day One

Pages 81–82 • Family Times

RD.2.1.6 Read aloud fluently and accurately with appropriate changes in voice and expression.

RD.2.2.6 Recognize cause-and-effect relationships in a text.

LS.2.7.10 Recount experiences or present stories that: move through a logical sequence of events; describe story elements, including characters, plot, and setting.

Page 83 • Plurals

RD.2.1.2 Recognize and use knowledge of spelling patterns (such as *cut/cutting, slide/sliding*) when reading.

RD.2.1.3 Decode (sound out) regular words with more than one syllable (*dinosaur, vacation*).

RD.2.1.5 Identify and correctly use regular plural words (*mountain/mountains*) and irregular plural words (*child/children, mouse/mice*).

Page 84 • Author's Purpose

RD.2.2.3 Use knowledge of the author's purpose(s) to comprehend informational text.

RD.2.3.4.3 Understand or interpret what is read or heard by responding to questions (*who, what, when, where, why, how*) and by using appropriate comprehension strategies, such as drawing conclusions, identifying the author's purpose, relating to prior knowledge, restating details, or setting a purpose for reading.

Day Two

Page 85 • Author's Purpose

RD.2.2.3 Use knowledge of the author's purpose(s) to comprehend informational text.

RD.2.3.4.3 Understand or interpret what is read or heard by responding to questions (*who, what, when, where, why, how*) and by using appropriate comprehension strategies, such as drawing conclusions, identifying the author's purpose, relating to prior knowledge, restating details, or setting a purpose for reading.

Page 86 • High-Frequency and Selection Words

RD.2.1.2 Recognize and use knowledge of spelling patterns (such as *cut/cutting, slide/sliding*) when reading.

RD.2.1.3 Decode (sound out) regular words with more than one syllable (*dinosaur, vacation*).

RD.2.1.5 Identify and correctly use regular plural words (*mountain/mountains*) and irregular plural words (*child/children, mouse/mice*).

RD.2.1.10 Identify simple multiple-meaning words (*change, duck*).

Page 87 • Realism and Fantasy

RD.2.2.2 State the purpose for reading.

RD.2.3.4.1 Recognize the difference between fantasy and reality.

Day Three

Page 88 • *r*-Controlled *er, ir, ur*

RD.2.1.1 Demonstrate an awareness of the sounds that are made by different letters by: distinguishing beginning, middle, and ending sounds in words; rhyming words; clearly pronouncing blends and vowel sounds.

RD.2.1.3 Decode (sound out) regular words with more than one syllable (*dinosaur, vacation*).

WR.2.6.9 Spell correctly words with short- and long-vowel sounds (*a, e, i, o, u*), *r*-controlled vowels (*ar, er, ir, or, ur*), and consonant-blend patterns (*bl, dr, st*).

Page 89 • High-Frequency Words

RD.2.1.2 Recognize and use knowledge of spelling patterns (such as *cut/cutting, slide/sliding*) when reading.

RD.2.1.5 Identify and correctly use regular plural words (*mountain/mountains*) and irregular plural words (*child/children, mouse/mice*).

WR.2.4.4 Understand the purposes of various reference materials (such as a dictionary, thesaurus, or atlas).

Day Five

Page 90 • Poster

WR.2.4.1 Create a list of ideas for writing.

WR.2.6.1 Form letters correctly and space words and sentences properly so that writing can be read easily by another person.

Unit 2 • A Turkey for Thanksgiving

Day One

Pages 91–92 • Family Times

RD.2.1.6 Read aloud fluently and accurately with appropriate changes in voice and expression.

RD.2.2.6 Recognize cause-and-effect relationships in a text.

RD.2.3.2 Create different endings to stories (predictions) and identify the reason (problem) and the impact of the different ending (solution).

Page 93 • Long *a: a, ai, ay*

RD.2.1.1 Demonstrate an awareness of the sounds that are made by different letters by: distinguishing beginning, middle, and ending sounds in words; rhyming words; clearly pronouncing blends and vowel sounds.

RD.2.1.2 Recognize and use knowledge of spelling patterns (such as *cut/cutting, slide/sliding*) when reading.

WR.2.6.9 Spell correctly words with short- and long-vowel sounds (*a, e, i, o, u*), *r*-controlled vowels (*ar, er, ir, or, ur*), and consonant-blend patterns (*bl, dr, st*).

Page 94 • Draw Conclusions

RD.2.2.8.1 Understand or interpret what is read or heard by continuing to use comprehension strategies such as those involving context, drawing conclusions, or prior knowledge.

RD.2.3.4.3 Understand or interpret what is read or heard by responding to questions (*who, what, when, where, why, how*) and by using appropriate comprehension strategies, such as drawing conclusions, identifying the author's purpose, relating to prior knowledge, restating details, or setting a purpose for reading.

Day Two

Page 95 • Draw Conclusions

RD.2.2.8.1 Understand or interpret what is read or heard by continuing to use comprehension strategies such as those involving context, drawing conclusions, or prior knowledge.

RD.2.3.4.3 Understand or interpret what is read or heard by responding to questions (*who, what, when, where, why, how*) and by using appropriate comprehension strategies, such as drawing conclusions, identifying the author's purpose, relating to prior knowledge, restating details, or setting a purpose for reading.

Page 96 • High-Frequency and Selection Words

RD.2.1.3 Decode (sound out) regular words with more than one syllable (*dinosaur, vacation*).

RD.2.1.5 Identify and correctly use regular plural words (*mountain/mountains*) and irregular plural words (*child/children, mouse/mice*).

RD.2.1.10 Identify simple multiple-meaning words (*change, duck*).

Page 97 • Author's Purpose

RD.2.2.3 Use knowledge of the author's purpose(s) to comprehend informational text.

RD.2.3.4.3 Understand or interpret what is read or heard by responding to questions (*who, what, when, where, why, how*) and by using appropriate comprehension strategies, such as drawing conclusions, identifying the author's purpose, relating to prior knowledge, restating details, or setting a purpose for reading.

Day Three

Page 98 • Plurals

RD.2.1.2 Recognize and use knowledge of spelling patterns (such as *cut/cutting, slide/sliding*) when reading.

RD.2.1.3 Decode (sound out) regular words with more than one syllable (*dinosaur, vacation*).

RD.2.1.5 Identify and correctly use regular plural words (*mountain/mountains*) and irregular plural words (*child/children, mouse/mice*).

Day Five

Page 99 • High-Frequency Words

RD.2.1.2 Recognize and use knowledge of spelling patterns (such as *cut/cutting, slide/sliding*) when reading.

RD.2.1.7 Understand and explain common synonyms (words with the same meaning) and antonyms (words with opposite meanings).

WR.2.4.4 Understand the purposes of various reference materials (such as a dictionary, thesaurus, or atlas).

Day Five

Page 100 • Web Page

WR.2.4.4 Understand the purposes of various reference materials (such as a dictionary, thesaurus, or atlas).

WR.2.4.5 Use a computer to draft, revise, and publish writing.

Unit 3 • Pearl and Wagner: Two Good Friends

Day One

Pages 101–102 • Family Times

RD.2.1.6 Read aloud fluently and accurately with appropriate changes in voice and expression.

LS.2.7.7 Tell experiences in a logical order.

LS.2.7.8 Retell stories, including characters, setting, and plot.

Page 103 • Long e

RD.2.1.1 Demonstrate an awareness of the sounds that are made by different letters by: distinguishing beginning, middle, and ending sounds in words; rhyming words; clearly pronouncing blends and vowel sounds.

RD.2.1.2 Recognize and use knowledge of spelling patterns (such as *cut/cutting, slide/sliding*) when reading.

WR.2.6.9 Spell correctly words with short- and long-vowel sounds (*a, e, i, o, u*), *r*-controlled vowels (*ar, er, ir, or, ur*), and consonant-blend patterns (*bl, dr, st*).

Page 104 • Author's Purpose

RD.2.2.3 Use knowledge of the author's purpose(s) to comprehend informational text.

RD.2.3.4.3 Understand or interpret what is read or heard by responding to questions (*who, what, when, where, why, how*) and by using appropriate comprehension strategies, such as drawing conclusions, identifying the author's purpose, relating to prior knowledge, restating details, or setting a purpose for reading.

Day Two

Page 105 • Author's Purpose

RD.2.2.3 Use knowledge of the author's purpose(s) to comprehend informational text.

RD.2.3.4.3 Understand or interpret what is read or heard by responding to questions (*who, what, when, where, why, how*) and by using appropriate comprehension strategies, such as drawing conclusions, identifying the author's purpose, relating to prior knowledge, restating details, or setting a purpose for reading.

Page 106 • High-Frequency Words

RD.2.1.2 Recognize and use knowledge of spelling patterns (such as *cut/cutting, slide/sliding*) when reading.

RD.2.1.3 Decode (sound out) regular words with more than one syllable (*dinosaur, vacation*).

RD.2.1.7 Understand and explain common synonyms (words with the same meaning) and antonyms (words with opposite meanings).

Page 107 • Sequence

RD.2.2.1.1 Identify text that uses sequence or other logical order (alphabetical order, time).

LS.2.7.7 Tell experiences in a logical order.

LS.2.7.10 Recount experiences or present stories that: move through a logical sequence of events; describe story elements, including characters, plot, and setting.

Day Three

Page 108 • Long *a: a, ai, ay*

RD.2.1.1 Demonstrate an awareness of the sounds that are made by different letters by: distinguishing beginning, middle, and ending sounds in words; rhyming words; clearly pronouncing blends and vowel sounds.

RD.2.1.2 Recognize and use knowledge of spelling patterns (such as *cut/cutting, slide/sliding*) when reading.

WR.2.6.9 Spell correctly words with short- and long-vowel sounds (*a, e, i, o, u*), *r*-controlled vowels (*ar, er, ir, or, ur*), and consonant-blend patterns (*bl, dr, st*).

Page 109 • High-Frequency Words

RD.2.1.3 Decode (sound out) regular words with more than one syllable (*dinosaur, vacation*).

RD.2.1.5 Identify and correctly use regular plural words (*mountain/mountains*) and irregular plural words (*child/children, mouse/mice*).

RD.2.1.8 Use knowledge of individual words to predict the meaning of unknown compound words (*lunchtime, lunchroom, daydream, raindrop*).

Day Five

Page 110 • Glossary Entry

RD.2.2.7 Interpret information from diagrams, charts, and graphs.

WR.2.4.4 Understand the purposes of various reference materials (such as a dictionary, thesaurus, or atlas).

Unit 3 • Dear Juno

Day One

Pages 111–112 • Family Times

RD.2.1.6 Read aloud fluently and accurately with appropriate changes in voice and expression.

RD.2.2.5 Restate facts and details or summarize the main idea in the text to clarify and organize ideas.

LS.2.7.8 Retell stories, including characters, setting, and plot.

Page 113 • Long o: o, oa, ow

RD.2.1.1 Demonstrate an awareness of the sounds that are made by different letters by: distinguishing beginning, middle, and ending sounds in words; rhyming words; clearly pronouncing blends and vowel sounds.

RD.2.1.2 Recognize and use knowledge of spelling patterns (such as *cut/cutting, slide/sliding*) when reading.

WR.2.6.9 Spell correctly words with short- and long-vowel sounds (*a, e, i, o, u*), r-controlled vowels (*ar, er, ir, or, ur*), and consonant-blend patterns (*bl, dr, st*).

Page 114 • Draw Conclusions

RD.2.2.8.1 Understand or interpret what is read or heard by continuing to use comprehension strategies such as those involving context, drawing conclusions, or prior knowledge.

RD.2.3.4.3 Understand or interpret what is read or heard by responding to questions (*who, what, when, where, why, how*) and by using appropriate comprehension strategies, such as drawing conclusions, identifying the author's purpose, relating to prior knowledge, restating details, or setting a purpose for reading.

Day Two

Page 115 • Draw Conclusions

RD.2.2.8.1 Understand or interpret what is read or heard by continuing to use comprehension strategies such as those involving context, drawing conclusions, or prior knowledge.

RD.2.3.4.3 Understand or interpret what is read or heard by responding to questions (*who, what, when, where, why, how*) and by using appropriate comprehension strategies, such as drawing conclusions, identifying the author's purpose, relating to prior knowledge, restating details, or setting a purpose for reading.

Page 116 • High-Frequency and Selection Words

RD.2.1.3 Decode (sound out) regular words with more than one syllable (*dinosaur, vacation*).

RD.2.1.5 Identify and correctly use regular plural words (*mountain/mountains*) and irregular plural words (*child/children, mouse/mice*).

RD.2.1.7 Understand and explain common synonyms (words with the same meaning) and antonyms (words with opposite meanings).

Page 117 • Author's Purpose

RD.2.2.3 Use knowledge of the author's purpose(s) to comprehend informational text.

RD.2.3.4.3 Understand or interpret what is read or heard by responding to questions (*who, what, when, where, why, how*) and by using appropriate comprehension strategies, such as drawing conclusions, identifying the author's purpose, relating to prior knowledge, restating details, or setting a purpose for reading.

Day Three

Page 118 • Long e: e, ee, ea, y

RD.2.1.1 Demonstrate an awareness of the sounds that are made by different letters by: distinguishing beginning, middle, and ending sounds in words; rhyming words; clearly pronouncing blends and vowel sounds.

RD.2.1.2 Recognize and use knowledge of spelling patterns (such as *cut/cutting, slide/sliding*) when reading.

WR.2.6.9 Spell correctly words with short- and long-vowel sounds (*a, e, i, o, u*), r-controlled vowels (*ar, er, ir, or, ur*), and consonant-blend patterns (*bl, dr, st*).

Page 119 • High-Frequency Words

RD.2.1.3 Decode (sound out) regular words with more than one syllable (*dinosaur, vacation*).

RD.2.1.7 Understand and explain common synonyms (words with the same meaning) and antonyms (words with opposite meanings).

RD.2.1.8 Use knowledge of individual words to predict the meaning of unknown compound words (*lunchtime, lunchroom, daydream, raindrop*).

Day Five

Page 120 • Globe

WR.2.4.4 Understand the purposes of various reference materials (such as a dictionary, thesaurus, or atlas).

LS.2.7.11 Report on a topic with facts and details, drawing from several sources of information.

Unit 3 • Anansi Goes Fishing

Day One

Pages 121–122 • Family Times

RD.2.2.6 Recognize cause-and-effect relationships in a text.

LS.2.7.7 Tell experiences in a logical order.

LS.2.7.10 Recount experiences or present stories that: move through a logical sequence of events; describe story elements, including characters, plot, and setting.

Page 123 • Compound Words

RD.2.1.2 Recognize and use knowledge of spelling patterns (such as *cut/cutting, slide/sliding*) when reading.

RD.2.1.3 Decode (sound out) regular words with more than one syllable (*dinosaur, vacation*).

RD.2.1.8 Use knowledge of individual words to predict the meaning of unknown compound words (*lunchtime, lunchroom, daydream, raindrop*).

Page 124 • Cause and Effect

RD.2.2.6 Recognize cause-and-effect relationships in a text.

LS.2.7.3 Paraphrase (restate in own words) information that has been shared orally by others.

LS.2.7.7 Tell experiences in a logical order.

Day Two

Page 125 • Cause and Effect

RD.2.2.6 Recognize cause-and-effect relationships in a text.

LS.2.7.8 Retell stories, including characters, setting, and plot.

LS.2.7.10 Recount experiences or present stories that: move through a logical sequence of events; describe story elements, including characters, plot, and setting.

Page 126 • High-Frequency Words

RD.2.1.7 Understand and explain common synonyms (words with the same meaning) and antonyms (words with opposite meanings).

RD.2.1.10 Identify simple multiple-meaning words (*change, duck*).

WR.2.6.8 Spell correctly words like *was, were, says, said, who, what,* and *why,* which are used frequently but do not fit common spelling patterns.

Page 127 • Draw Conclusions

RD.2.2.8.1 Understand or interpret what is read or heard by continuing to use comprehension strategies such as those involving context, drawing conclusions, or prior knowledge.

RD.2.3.4.3 Understand or interpret what is read or heard by responding to questions (*who, what, when, where, why, how*) and by using appropriate comprehension strategies, such as drawing conclusions, identifying the author's purpose, relating to prior knowledge, restating details, or setting a purpose for reading.

Day Three

Page 128 • Long o: o, oa, and ow

RD.2.1.1 Demonstrate an awareness of the sounds that are made by different letters by: distinguishing beginning, middle, and ending sounds in words; rhyming words; clearly pronouncing blends and vowel sounds.

WR.2.6.9 Spell correctly words with short- and long-vowel sounds (*a, e, i, o, u*), r-controlled vowels (*ar, er, ir, or, ur*), and consonant-blend patterns (*bl, dr, st*).

Page 129 • High-Frequency Words

RD.2.1.2 Recognize and use knowledge of spelling patterns (such as *cut/cutting, slide/sliding*) when reading.

RD.2.1.8 Use knowledge of individual words to predict the meaning of unknown compound words (*lunchtime, lunchroom, daydream, raindrop*).

RD.2.1.10 Identify simple multiple-meaning words (*change, duck*).

Day Five

Page 130 • Alphabetical Order

WR.2.4.2 Organize related ideas together to maintain a consistent focus.

WR.2.4.4 Understand the purposes of various reference materials (such as a dictionary, thesaurus, or atlas).

Unit 3 • Rosa and Blanca

Day One

Pages 131–132 • Family Times

RD.2.2.6 Recognize cause-and-effect relationships in a text.

LS.2.7.8 Retell stories, including characters, setting, and plot.

LS.2.7.10 Recount experiences or present stories that: move through a logical sequence of events; describe story elements, including characters, plot, and setting.

Page 133 • Long *i: i, ie, y, igh*

RD.2.1.1 Demonstrate an awareness of the sounds that are made by different letters by: distinguishing beginning, middle, and ending sounds in words; rhyming words; clearly pronouncing blends and vowel sounds.

RD.2.1.2 Recognize and use knowledge of spelling patterns (such as *cut/cutting, slide/sliding*) when reading.

WR.2.6.9 Spell correctly words with short- and long-vowel sounds (*a, e, i, o, u*), *r*-controlled vowels (*ar, er, ir, or, ur*), and consonant-blend patterns (*bl, dr, st*).

Page 134 • Theme and Plot

RD.2.3.4.2 Discuss the author's main message (theme) of a story.

LS.2.7.8 Retell stories, including characters, setting, and plot.

LS.2.7.10 Recount experiences or present stories that: move through a logical sequence of events; describe story elements, including characters, plot, and setting.

Day Two

Page 135 • Theme and Plot

RD.2.3.4.2 Discuss the author's main message (theme) of a story.

LS.2.7.8 Retell stories, including characters, setting, and plot.

LS.2.7.10 Recount experiences or present stories that: move through a logical sequence of events; describe story elements, including characters, plot, and setting.

Page 136 • High-Frequency Words

RD.2.1.7 Understand and explain common synonyms (words with the same meaning) and antonyms (words with opposite meanings).

RD.2.1.10 Identify simple multiple-meaning words (*change, duck*).

WR.2.6.8 Spell correctly words like *was, were, says, said, who, what,* and *why,* which are used frequently but do not fit common spelling patterns.

Page 137 • Cause and Effect

RD.2.2.5 Restate facts and details or summarize the main idea in the text to clarify and organize ideas.

RD.2.2.6 Recognize cause-and-effect relationships in a text.

LS.2.7.10 Recount experiences or present stories that: move through a logical sequence of events; describe story elements, including characters, plot, and setting.

Day Three

Page 138 • Compound Words

RD.2.1.3 Decode (sound out) regular words with more than one syllable (*dinosaur, vacation*).

RD.2.1.8 Use knowledge of individual words to predict the meaning of unknown compound words (*lunchtime, lunchroom, daydream, raindrop*).

Page 139 • High-Frequency Words

RD.2.1.2 Recognize and use knowledge of spelling patterns (such as *cut/cutting, slide/sliding*) when reading.

RD.2.1.5 Identify and correctly use regular plural words (*mountain/mountains*) and irregular plural words (*child/children, mouse/mice*).

RD.2.1.8 Use knowledge of individual words to predict the meaning of unknown compound words (*lunchtime, lunchroom, daydream, raindrop*).

Day Five

Page 140 • Tally Chart

RD.2.2.7 Interpret information from diagrams, charts, and graphs.

WR.2.4.2 Organize related ideas together to maintain a consistent focus.

Unit 3 • A Weed Is a Flower

Day One

Pages 141–142 • Family Times

RD.2.2.5 Restate facts and details or summarize the main idea in the text to clarify and organize ideas.

LS.2.7.9 Report on a topic with supportive facts and details.

LS.2.7.10 Recount experiences or present stories that: move through a logical sequence of events; describe story elements, including characters, plot, and setting.

Page 143 • Comparative Endings

RD.2.1.2 Recognize and use knowledge of spelling patterns (such as *cut/cutting, slide/sliding*) when reading.

RD.2.1.3 Decode (sound out) regular words with more than one syllable (*dinosaur, vacation*).

WR.2.6.8 Spell correctly words like *was, were, says, said, who, what,* and *why,* which are used frequently but do not fit common spelling patterns.

Page 144 • Cause and Effect

RD.2.2.3 Use knowledge of the author's purpose(s) to comprehend informational text.

RD.2.2.4 Ask and respond to questions (*why, what if, how*) to aid comprehension about important elements of informational texts.

RD.2.2.6 Recognize cause-and-effect relationships in a text.

Day Two

Page 145 • Cause and Effect

RD.2.2.4 Ask and respond to questions (*why, what if, how*) to aid comprehension about important elements of informational texts.

RD.2.2.5 Restate facts and details or summarize the main idea in the text to clarify and organize ideas.

RD.2.2.6 Recognize cause-and-effect relationships in a text.

Page 146 • High-Frequency and Selection Words

RD.2.1.3 Decode (sound out) regular words with more than one syllable (*dinosaur, vacation*).

RD.2.1.7 Understand and explain common synonyms (words with the same meaning) and antonyms (words with opposite meanings).

Page 147 • Draw Conclusions

RD.2.2.8.1 Understand or interpret what is read or heard by continuing to use comprehension strategies such as those involving context, drawing conclusions, or prior knowledge.

RD.2.3.4.3 Understand or interpret what is read or heard by responding to questions (*who, what, when, where, why, how*) and by using appropriate comprehension strategies, such as drawing conclusions, identifying the author's purpose, relating to prior knowledge, restating details, or setting a purpose for reading.

Day Three

Page 148 • Long *i*

RD.2.1.1 Demonstrate an awareness of the sounds that are made by different letters by: distinguishing beginning, middle, and ending sounds in words; rhyming words; clearly pronouncing blends and vowel sounds.

RD.2.1.3 Decode (sound out) regular words with more than one syllable (*dinosaur, vacation*).

WR.2.6.9 Spell correctly words with short- and long-vowel sounds (*a, e, i, o, u*), *r*-controlled vowels (*ar, er, ir, or, ur*), and consonant-blend patterns (*bl, dr, st*).

Page 149 • High-Frequency Words

RD.2.1.3 Decode (sound out) regular words with more than one syllable (*dinosaur, vacation*).

RD.2.1.6 Read aloud fluently and accurately with appropriate changes in voice and expression.

RD.2.1.7 Understand and explain common synonyms (words with the same meaning) and antonyms (words with opposite meanings).

Day Five

Page 150 • Search the Internet

WR.2.4.5 Use a computer to draft, revise, and publish writing.

LS.2.7.11 Report on a topic with facts and details, drawing from several sources of information.

Unit 4 • The Quilt Story

Day One

Pages 1–2 • Family Times

RD.2.2.5 Restate facts and details or summarize the main idea in the text to clarify and organize ideas.

LS.2.7.7 Tell experiences in a logical order.

LS.2.7.8 Retell stories, including characters, setting, and plot.

Page 3 • Consonant + le

RD.2.1.1 Demonstrate an awareness of the sounds that are made by different letters by: distinguishing beginning, middle, and ending sounds in words; rhyming words; clearly pronouncing blends and vowel sounds.

RD.2.1.2 Recognize and use knowledge of spelling patterns (such as *cut/cutting, slide/sliding*) when reading.

RD.2.1.3 Decode (sound out) regular words with more than one syllable (*dinosaur, vacation*).

Page 4 • Compare and Contrast

RD.2.2.1 Use titles, tables of contents, and chapter headings to locate information in text.

RD.2.2.4 Ask and respond to questions (*why, what if, how*) to aid comprehension about important elements of informational texts.

RD.2.2.6 Recognize cause-and-effect relationships in a text.

Day Two

Page 5 • Compare and Contrast

RD.2.2.5 Restate facts and details or summarize the main idea in the text to clarify and organize ideas.

RD.2.3.3 Compare versions of same stories from different cultures.

LS.2.7.9 Report on a topic with supportive facts and details.

Page 6 • Lesson Vocabulary

RD.2.1.3 Decode (sound out) regular words with more than one syllable (*dinosaur, vacation*).

RD.2.1.6 Read aloud fluently and accurately with appropriate changes in voice and expression.

RD.2.1.7 Understand and explain common synonyms (words with the same meaning) and antonyms (words with opposite meanings).

Page 7 • Character and Setting

RD.2.3.1 Compare plots, settings, and characters presented by different authors.

LS.2.7.8 Retell stories, including characters, setting, and plot.

LS.2.7.10 Recount experiences or present stories that: move through a logical sequence of events; describe story elements, including characters, plot, and setting.

Day Three

Page 8 • Comparative Endings

RD.2.1.1 Demonstrate an awareness of the sounds that are made by different letters by: distinguishing beginning, middle, and ending sounds in words; rhyming words; clearly pronouncing blends and vowel sounds.

RD.2.1.2 Recognize and use knowledge of spelling patterns (such as *cut/cutting, slide/sliding*) when reading.

RD.2.1.3 Decode (sound out) regular words with more than one syllable (*dinosaur, vacation*).

Page 9 • Lesson Vocabulary

RD.2.1.6 Read aloud fluently and accurately with appropriate changes in voice and expression.

RD.2.1.7 Understand and explain common synonyms (words with the same meaning) and antonyms (words with opposite meanings).

WR.2.4.4 Understand the purposes of various reference materials (such as a dictionary, thesaurus, or atlas).

Day Five

Page 10 • Reference Sources

RD.2.2.1 Use titles, tables of contents, and chapter headings to locate information in text.

WR.2.4.4 Understand the purposes of various reference materials (such as a dictionary, thesaurus, or atlas).

LS.2.7.11 Report on a topic with facts and details, drawing from several sources of information.

Unit 4 • Life Cycle of a Pumpkin

Day One

Pages 11–12 • Family Times

RD.2.2.5 Restate facts and details or summarize the main idea in the text to clarify and organize ideas.

LS.2.7.8 Retell stories, including characters, setting, and plot.

Page 13 • Vowels oo, u

RD.2.1.1 Demonstrate an awareness of the sounds that are made by different letters by: distinguishing beginning, middle, and ending sounds in words; rhyming words; clearly pronouncing blends and vowel sounds.

RD.2.1.2 Recognize and use knowledge of spelling patterns (such as *cut/cutting, slide/sliding*) when reading.

WR.2.6.9 Spell correctly words with short- and long-vowel sounds (*a, e, i, o, u*), *r*-controlled vowels (*ar, er, ir, or, ur*), and consonant-blend patterns (*bl, dr, st*).

Page 14 • Fact and Opinion

RD.2.2.3 Use knowledge of the author's purpose(s) to comprehend informational text.

RD.2.2.4 Ask and respond to questions (*why, what if, how*) to aid comprehension about important elements of informational texts.

RD.2.2.5 Restate facts and details or summarize the main idea in the text to clarify and organize ideas.

Day Two

Page 15 • Fact and Opinion

RD.2.2.3 Use knowledge of the author's purpose(s) to comprehend informational text.

RD.2.2.4 Ask and respond to questions (*why, what if, how*) to aid comprehension about important elements of informational texts.

LS.2.7.9 Report on a topic with supportive facts and details.

Page 16 • Lesson Vocabulary

RD.2.1.2 Recognize and use knowledge of spelling patterns (such as *cut/cutting, slide/sliding*) when reading.

RD.2.1.8 Use knowledge of individual words to predict the meaning of unknown compound words (*lunchtime, lunchroom, daydream, raindrop*).

RD.2.1.10 Identify simple multiple-meaning words (*change, duck*).

Page 17 • Compare and Contrast

RD.2.2.5 Restate facts and details or summarize the main idea in the text to clarify and organize ideas.

LS.2.7.9 Report on a topic with supportive facts and details.

Day Three

Page 18 • C + *le*

RD.2.1.2 Recognize and use knowledge of spelling patterns (such as *cut/cutting, slide/sliding*) when reading.

RD.2.1.3 Decode (sound out) regular words with more than one syllable (*dinosaur, vacation*).

WR.2.6.8 Spell correctly words like *was, were, says, said, who, what,* and *why*, which are used frequently but do not fit common spelling patterns.

Page 19 • Lesson Vocabulary

RD.2.1.6 Read aloud fluently and accurately with appropriate changes in voice and expression.

RD.2.1.7 Understand and explain common synonyms (words with the same meaning) and antonyms (words with opposite meanings).

RD.2.1.8 Use knowledge of individual words to predict the meaning of unknown compound words (*lunchtime, lunchroom, daydream, raindrop*).

Day Five

Page 20 • Circle Graph

RD.2.2.7 Interpret information from diagrams, charts, and graphs.

WR.2.4.2 Organize related ideas together to maintain a consistent focus.

Unit 4 • Frogs

Day One

Pages 21–22 • Family Times

RD.2.1.6 Read aloud fluently and accurately with appropriate changes in voice and expression.

LS.2.7.7 Tell experiences in a logical order.

LS.2.7.9 Report on a topic with supportive facts and details.

Page 23 • Diphthongs *ou, ow/ou/*

RD.2.1.1 Demonstrate an awareness of the sounds that are made by different letters by: distinguishing beginning, middle, and ending sounds in words; rhyming words; clearly pronouncing blends and vowel sounds.

RD.2.1.2 Recognize and use knowledge of spelling patterns (such as *cut/cutting, slide/sliding*) when reading.

WR.2.6.9 Spell correctly words with short- and long-vowel sounds (*a, e, i, o, u*), r-controlled vowels (*ar, er, ir, or, ur*), and consonant-blend patterns (*bl, dr, st*).

Page 24 • Compare and Contrast

RD.2.2.5 Restate facts and details or summarize the main idea in the text to clarify and organize ideas.

RD.2.2.6 Recognize cause-and-effect relationships in a text.

LS.2.7.9 Report on a topic with supportive facts and details.

Day Two

Page 25 • Compare and Contrast

RD.2.2.4 Ask and respond to questions (*why, what if, how*) to aid comprehension about important elements of informational texts.

RD.2.2.5 Restate facts and details or summarize the main idea in the text to clarify and organize ideas.

RD.2.2.6 Recognize cause-and-effect relationships in a text.

Page 26 • Lesson Vocabulary

RD.2.1.2 Recognize and use knowledge of spelling patterns (such as *cut/cutting, slide/sliding*) when reading.

RD.2.1.5 Identify and correctly use regular plural words (*mountain/mountains*) and irregular plural words (*child/children, mouse/mice*).

RD.2.1.8 Use knowledge of individual words to predict the meaning of unknown compound words (*lunchtime, lunchroom, daydream, raindrop*).

Page 27 • Fact and Opinion

RD.2.2.3 Use knowledge of the author's purpose(s) to comprehend informational text.

RD.2.2.4 Ask and respond to questions (*why, what if, how*) to aid comprehension about important elements of informational texts.

RD.2.2.5 Restate facts and details or summarize the main idea in the text to clarify and organize ideas.

Day Three

Page 28 • Vowels *oo, u*

RD.2.1.1 Demonstrate an awareness of the sounds that are made by different letters by: distinguishing beginning, middle, and ending sounds in words; rhyming words; clearly pronouncing blends and vowel sounds.

RD.2.1.2 Recognize and use knowledge of spelling patterns (such as *cut/cutting, slide/sliding*) when reading.

WR.2.6.9 Spell correctly words with short- and long-vowel sounds (*a, e, i, o, u*), r-controlled vowels (*ar, er, ir, or, ur*), and consonant-blend patterns (*bl, dr, st*).

Page 29 • Lesson Vocabulary

RD.2.1.6 Read aloud fluently and accurately with appropriate changes in voice and expression.

RD.2.1.7 Understand and explain common synonyms (words with the same meaning) and antonyms (words with opposite meanings).

Day Five

Page 30 • Diagram

RD.2.2.7 Interpret information from diagrams, charts, and graphs.

WR.2.4.3 Find ideas for writing stories and descriptions in pictures or books.

Unit 4 • I Like Where I Am

Day One

Pages 31–32 • Family Times

RD.2.1.6 Read aloud fluently and accurately with appropriate changes in voice and expression.

LS.2.7.7 Tell experiences in a logical order.

LS.2.7.9 Report on a topic with supportive facts and details.

Page 33 • Vowel Diphthongs *oi* and *oy/oi/*

RD.2.1.1 Demonstrate an awareness of the sounds that are made by different letters by: distinguishing beginning, middle, and ending sounds in words; rhyming words; clearly pronouncing blends and vowel sounds.

RD.2.1.2 Recognize and use knowledge of spelling patterns (such as *cut/cutting, slide/sliding*) when reading.

Page 34 • Theme and Plot

RD.2.3.4.2 Discuss the author's main message (theme) of a story.

LS.2.7.8 Retell stories, including characters, setting, and plot.

LS.2.7.10 Recount experiences or present stories that: move through a logical sequence of events; describe story elements, including characters, plot, and setting.

Day Two

Page 35 • Theme and Plot

RD.2.3.4.2 Discuss the author's main message (theme) of a story.

LS.2.7.8 Retell stories, including characters, setting, and plot.

LS.2.7.10 Recount experiences or present stories that: move through a logical sequence of events; describe story elements, including characters, plot, and setting.

Page 36 • Lesson Vocabulary

RD.2.1.2 Recognize and use knowledge of spelling patterns (such as *cut/cutting, slide/sliding*) when reading.

RD.2.1.5 Identify and correctly use regular plural words (*mountain/mountains*) and irregular plural words (*child/children, mouse/mice*).

WR.2.6.8 Spell correctly words like *was*, *were*, *says*, *said*, *who*, *what*, and *why*, which are used frequently but do not fit common spelling patterns.

Page 37 • Draw Conclusions

RD.2.2.8.1 Understand or interpret what is read or heard by continuing to use comprehension strategies such as those involving context, drawing conclusions, or prior knowledge.

RD.2.3.4.3 Understand or interpret what is read or heard by responding to questions (*who*, *what*, *when*, *where*, *why*, *how*) and by using appropriate comprehension strategies, such as drawing conclusions, identifying the author's purpose, relating to prior knowledge, restating details, or setting a purpose for reading.

Day Three

Page 38 • Diphthongs *ou*, *ow/ou/*

RD.2.1.1 Demonstrate an awareness of the sounds that are made by different letters by: distinguishing beginning, middle, and ending sounds in words; rhyming words; clearly pronouncing blends and vowel sounds.

RD.2.1.2 Recognize and use knowledge of spelling patterns (such as *cut/cutting*, *slide/sliding*) when reading.

Page 39 • Lesson Vocabulary

RD.2.1.2 Recognize and use knowledge of spelling patterns (such as *cut/cutting*, *slide/sliding*) when reading.

RD.2.1.7 Understand and explain common synonyms (words with the same meaning) and antonyms (words with opposite meanings).

RD.2.1.8 Use knowledge of individual words to predict the meaning of unknown compound words (*lunchtime*, *lunchroom*, *daydream*, *raindrop*).

Day Five

Page 40 • E-mail

WR.2.4.1 Create a list of ideas for writing.

WR.2.4.5 Use a computer to draft, revise, and publish writing.

Unit 4 • Helen Keller and the Big Storm

Day One

Pages 41–42 • Family Times

RD.2.2.5 Restate facts and details or summarize the main idea in the text to clarify and organize ideas.

RD.2.2.6 Recognize cause-and-effect relationships in a text.

LS.2.7.9 Report on a topic with supportive facts and details.

Page 43 • Vowels

RD.2.1.1 Demonstrate an awareness of the sounds that are made by different letters by: distinguishing beginning, middle, and ending sounds in words; rhyming words; clearly pronouncing blends and vowel sounds.

RD.2.1.2 Recognize and use knowledge of spelling patterns (such as *cut/cutting*, *slide/sliding*) when reading.

WR.2.6.9 Spell correctly words with short- and long-vowel sounds (*a, e, i, o, u*), *r*-controlled vowels (*ar, er, ir, or, ur*), and consonant-blend patterns (*bl, dr, st*).

Page 44 • Fact and Opinion

RD.2.2.3 Use knowledge of the author's purpose(s) to comprehend informational text.

RD.2.2.4 Ask and respond to questions (*why, what if, how*) to aid comprehension about important elements of informational texts.

RD.2.2.5 Restate facts and details or summarize the main idea in the text to clarify and organize ideas.

Day Two

Page 45 • Fact and Opinion

RD.2.2.3 Use knowledge of the author's purpose(s) to comprehend informational text.

RD.2.2.4 Ask and respond to questions (*why, what if, how*) to aid comprehension about important elements of informational texts.

LS.2.7.9 Report on a topic with supportive facts and details.

Page 46 • Lesson Vocabulary

RD.2.1.2 Recognize and use knowledge of spelling patterns (such as *cut/cutting*, *slide/sliding*) when reading.

RD.2.1.10 Identify simple multiple-meaning words (*change, duck*).

WR.2.6.8 Spell correctly words like *was*, *were*, *says*, *said*, *who*, *what*, and *why*, which are used frequently but do not fit common spelling patterns.

Page 47 • Main Idea and Details

RD.2.2.3 Use knowledge of the author's purpose(s) to comprehend informational text.

RD.2.2.4 Ask and respond to questions (*why, what if, how*) to aid comprehension about important elements of informational texts.

RD.2.2.5 Restate facts and details or summarize the main idea in the text to clarify and organize ideas.

Day Three

Page 48 • Diphthongs *oi*, *oy/oi/*

RD.2.1.1 Demonstrate an awareness of the sounds that are made by different letters by: distinguishing beginning, middle, and ending sounds in words; rhyming words; clearly pronouncing blends and vowel sounds.

RD.2.1.2 Recognize and use knowledge of spelling patterns (such as *cut/cutting*, *slide/sliding*) when reading.

Page 49 • Lesson Vocabulary

RD.2.1.2 Recognize and use knowledge of spelling patterns (such as *cut/cutting*, *slide/sliding*) when reading.

RD.2.1.3 Decode (sound out) regular words with more than one syllable (*dinosaur, vacation*).

RD.2.1.7 Understand and explain common synonyms (words with the same meaning) and antonyms (words with opposite meanings).

Day Five

Page 50 • Reference Sources

RD.2.2.1 Use titles, tables of contents, and chapter headings to locate information in text.

WR.2.4.4 Understand the purposes of various reference materials (such as a dictionary, thesaurus, or atlas).

Unit 5 • Fire Fighter!

Day One

Pages 51–52 • Family Times

RD.2.2.5 Restate facts and details or summarize the main idea in the text to clarify and organize ideas.

LS.2.7.7 Tell experiences in a logical order.

LS.2.7.9 Report on a topic with supportive facts and details.

Page 53 • Suffixes -*ly*, -*ful*, -*er*, -*or*

RD.2.1.3 Decode (sound out) regular words with more than one syllable (*dinosaur, vacation*).

RD.2.1.9 Know the meaning of simple prefixes (word parts added at the beginning of words such as *un-*) and suffixes (word parts added at the end of words such as -*ful*).

Page 54 • Main Idea and Details

RD.2.2.4 Ask and respond to questions (*why, what if, how*) to aid comprehension about important elements of informational texts.

RD.2.2.5 Restate facts and details or summarize the main idea in the text to clarify and organize ideas.

LS.2.7.9 Report on a topic with supportive facts and details.

Day Two

Page 55 • Main Idea and Details

RD.2.2.3 Use knowledge of the author's purpose(s) to comprehend informational text.

RD.2.2.4 Ask and respond to questions (*why, what if, how*) to aid comprehension about important elements of informational texts.

RD.2.2.5 Restate facts and details or summarize the main idea in the text to clarify and organize ideas.

Page 56 • Lesson Vocabulary

RD.2.1.3 Decode (sound out) regular words with more than one syllable (*dinosaur, vacation*).

RD.2.1.6 Read aloud fluently and accurately with appropriate changes in voice and expression.

WR.2.6.8 Spell correctly words like *was*, *were*, *says*, *said*, *who*, *what*, and *why*, which are used frequently but do not fit common spelling patterns.

Page 57 • Author's Purpose

RD.2.2.3 Use knowledge of the author's purpose(s) to comprehend informational text.

RD.2.3.4.3 Understand or interpret what is read or heard by responding to questions (*who, what, when, where, why, how*) and by using appropriate comprehension strategies, such as drawing conclusions, identifying the author's purpose, relating to prior knowledge, restating details, or setting a purpose for reading.

Day Three

Page 58 • Vowel Patterns *oo, ue, ew, ui*

RD.2.1.1 Demonstrate an awareness of the sounds that are made by different letters by: distinguishing beginning, middle, and ending sounds in words; rhyming words; clearly pronouncing blends and vowel sounds.

RD.2.1.2 Recognize and use knowledge of spelling patterns (such as *cut/cutting, slide/sliding*) when reading.

Page 59 • Lesson Vocabulary

RD.2.1.5 Identify and correctly use regular plural words (*mountain/mountains*) and irregular plural words (*child/children, mouse/mice*).

RD.2.1.6 Read aloud fluently and accurately with appropriate changes in voice and expression.

RD.2.1.7 Understand and explain common synonyms (words with the same meaning) and antonyms (words with opposite meanings).

Day Five

Page 60 • Glossary

WR.2.4.4 Understand the purposes of various reference materials (such as a dictionary, thesaurus, or atlas).

LS.2.7.11 Report on a topic with facts and details, drawing from several sources of information.

Unit 5 • **One Dark Night**

Day One

Pages 61–62 • Family Times

RD.2.3.2 Create different endings to stories (predictions) and identify the reason (problem) and the impact of the different ending (solution).

LS.2.7.7 Tell experiences in a logical order.

LS.2.7.8 Retell stories, including characters, setting, and plot.

Page 63 • Prefixes

RD.2.1.2 Recognize and use knowledge of spelling patterns (such as *cut/cutting, slide/sliding*) when reading.

RD.2.1.3 Decode (sound out) regular words with more than one syllable (*dinosaur, vacation*).

RD.2.1.9 Know the meaning of simple prefixes (word parts added at the beginning of words such as *un-*) and suffixes (word parts added at the end of words such as *-ful*).

Page 64 • Sequence

RD.2.2.1.1 Identify text that uses sequence or other logical order (alphabetical order, time).

LS.2.7.7 Tell experiences in a logical order.

LS.2.7.10 Recount experiences or present stories that: move through a logical sequence of events; describe story elements, including characters, plot, and setting.

Day Two

Page 65 • Sequence

RD.2.2.1.1 Identify text that uses sequence or other logical order (alphabetical order, time).

LS.2.7.7 Tell experiences in a logical order.

LS.2.7.10 Recount experiences or present stories that: move through a logical sequence of events; describe story elements, including characters, plot, and setting.

Page 66 • Lesson Vocabulary

RD.2.1.5 Identify and correctly use regular plural words (*mountain/mountains*) and irregular plural words (*child/children, mouse/mice*).

RD.2.1.6 Read aloud fluently and accurately with appropriate changes in voice and expression.

RD.2.1.8 Use knowledge of individual words to predict the meaning of unknown compound words (*lunchtime, lunchroom, daydream, raindrop*).

Page 67 • Plot and Theme

RD.2.3.4.2 Discuss the author's main message (theme) of a story.

LS.2.7.8 Retell stories, including characters, setting, and plot.

LS.2.7.10 Recount experiences or present stories that: move through a logical sequence of events; describe story elements, including characters, plot, and setting.

Day Three

Page 68 • Suffixes *-ly, -ful, -er, -or*

RD.2.1.3 Decode (sound out) regular words with more than one syllable (*dinosaur, vacation*).

RD.2.1.9 Know the meaning of simple prefixes (word parts added at the beginning of words such as *un-*) and suffixes (word parts added at the end of words such as *-ful*).

Page 69 • Lesson Vocabulary

RD.2.1.5 Identify and correctly use regular plural words (*mountain/mountains*) and irregular plural words (*child/children, mouse/mice*).

RD.2.1.7 Understand and explain common synonyms (words with the same meaning) and antonyms (words with opposite meanings).

RD.2.1.10 Identify simple multiple-meaning words (*change, duck*).

Day Five

Page 70 • Bar Graph

RD.2.2.7 Interpret information from diagrams, charts, and graphs.

WR.2.4.2 Organize related ideas together to maintain a consistent focus.

Unit 5 • **Bad Dog, Dodger!**

Day One

Pages 71–72 • Family Times

RD.2.3.2 Create different endings to stories (predictions) and identify the reason (problem) and the impact of the different ending (solution).

LS.2.7.7 Tell experiences in a logical order.

LS.2.7.8 Retell stories, including characters, setting, and plot.

Page 73 • Silent Consonants

RD.2.1.1 Demonstrate an awareness of the sounds that are made by different letters by: distinguishing beginning, middle, and ending sounds in words; rhyming words; clearly pronouncing blends and vowel sounds.

RD.2.1.3 Decode (sound out) regular words with more than one syllable (*dinosaur, vacation*).

WR.2.6.8 Spell correctly words like *was*, *were*, *says*, *said*, *who*, *what*, and *why*, which are used frequently but do not fit common spelling patterns.

Page 74 • Plot and Theme

RD.2.3.4.2 Discuss the author's main message (theme) of a story.

LS.2.7.8 Retell stories, including characters, setting, and plot.

LS.2.7.10 Recount experiences or present stories that: move through a logical sequence of events; describe story elements, including characters, plot, and setting.

Day Two

Page 75 • Plot and Theme

RD.2.3.4.2 Discuss the author's main message (theme) of a story.

LS.2.7.8 Retell stories, including characters, setting, and plot.

LS.2.7.10 Recount experiences or present stories that: move through a logical sequence of events; describe story elements, including characters, plot, and setting.

Page 76 • Lesson Vocabulary

RD.2.1.5 Identify and correctly use regular plural words (*mountain/mountains*) and irregular plural words (*child/children, mouse/mice*).

RD.2.1.6 Read aloud fluently and accurately with appropriate changes in voice and expression.

RD.2.1.7 Understand and explain common synonyms (words with the same meaning) and antonyms (words with opposite meanings).

Page 77 • Sequence

RD.2.2.1.1 Identify text that uses sequence or other logical order (alphabetical order, time).

LS.2.7.7 Tell experiences in a logical order.

LS.2.7.10 Recount experiences or present stories that: move through a logical sequence of events; describe story elements, including characters, plot, and setting.

Day Three

Page 78 • Prefixes *un-, re-, pre-, dis-*

RD.2.1.2 Recognize and use knowledge of spelling patterns (such as *cut/cutting, slide/sliding*) when reading.

RD.2.1.3 Decode (sound out) regular words with more than one syllable (*dinosaur, vacation*).

RD.2.1.9 Know the meaning of simple prefixes (word parts added at the beginning of words such as *un-*) and suffixes (word parts added at the end of words such as *-ful*).

Page 79 • Lesson Vocabulary

RD.2.1.5 Identify and correctly use regular plural words (*mountain/mountains*) and irregular plural words (*child/children, mouse/mice*).

RD.2.1.7 Understand and explain common synonyms (words with the same meaning) and antonyms (words with opposite meanings).

WR.2.4.4 Understand the purposes of various reference materials (such as a dictionary, thesaurus, or atlas).

Day Five

Page 80 • Encyclopedia

WR.2.4.4 Understand the purposes of various reference materials (such as a dictionary, thesaurus, or atlas).

LS.2.7.11 Report on a topic with facts and details, drawing from several sources of information.

Unit 5 • Horace and Morris but mostly Dolores

Day One

Pages 81–82 • Family Times

RD.2.1.6 Read aloud fluently and accurately with appropriate changes in voice and expression.

RD.2.2.6 Recognize cause-and-effect relationships in a text.

LS.2.7.10 Recount experiences or present stories that: move through a logical sequence of events; describe story elements, including characters, plot, and setting.

Page 83 • *ph, gh/f/*

RD.2.1.1 Demonstrate an awareness of the sounds that are made by different letters by: distinguishing beginning, middle, and ending sounds in words; rhyming words; clearly pronouncing blends and vowel sounds.

WR.2.6.8 Spell correctly words like *was, were, says, said, who, what,* and *why,* which are used frequently but do not fit common spelling patterns.

Page 84 • Author's Purpose

RD.2.2.3 Use knowledge of the author's purpose(s) to comprehend informational text.

RD.2.3.4.3 Understand or interpret what is read or heard by responding to questions (*who, what, when, where, why, how*) and by using appropriate comprehension strategies, such as drawing conclusions, identifying the author's purpose, relating to prior knowledge, restating details, or setting a purpose for reading.

Day Two

Page 85 • Author's Purpose

RD.2.2.3 Use knowledge of the author's purpose(s) to comprehend informational text.

RD.2.3.4.3 Understand or interpret what is read or heard by responding to questions (*who, what, when, where, why, how*) and by using appropriate comprehension strategies, such as drawing conclusions, identifying the author's purpose, relating to prior knowledge, restating details, or setting a purpose for reading.

Page 86 • Lesson Vocabulary

RD.2.1.8 Use knowledge of individual words to predict the meaning of unknown compound words (*lunchtime, lunchroom, daydream, raindrop*).

RD.2.1.10 Identify simple multiple-meaning words (*change, duck*).

WR.2.6.8 Spell correctly words like *was, were, says, said, who, what,* and *why,* which are used frequently but do not fit common spelling patterns.

Page 87 • Plot and Theme

RD.2.3.4.2 Discuss the author's main message (theme) of a story.

LS.2.7.8 Retell stories, including characters, setting, and plot.

LS.2.7.10 Recount experiences or present stories that: move through a logical sequence of events; describe story elements, including characters, plot, and setting.

Day Three

Page 88 • Silent Consonants

RD.2.1.1 Demonstrate an awareness of the sounds that are made by different letters by: distinguishing beginning, middle, and ending sounds in words; rhyming words; clearly pronouncing blends and vowel sounds.

RD.2.1.3 Decode (sound out) regular words with more than one syllable (*dinosaur, vacation*).

WR.2.6.8 Spell correctly words like *was, were, says, said, who, what,* and *why,* which are used frequently but do not fit common spelling patterns.

Page 89 • Lesson Vocabulary

RD.2.1.5 Identify and correctly use regular plural words (*mountain/mountains*) and irregular plural words (*child/children, mouse/mice*).

RD.2.1.10 Identify simple multiple-meaning words (*change, duck*).

WR.2.4.4 Understand the purposes of various reference materials (such as a dictionary, thesaurus, or atlas).

Day Five

Page 90 • Tables

RD.2.2.1 Use titles, tables of contents, and chapter headings to locate information in text.

RD.2.2.7 Interpret information from diagrams, charts, and graphs.

Unit 5 • The Signmaker's Assistant

Day One

Pages 91–92 • Family Times

RD.2.2.6 Recognize cause-and-effect relationships in a text.

RD.2.3.2 Create different endings to stories (predictions) and identify the reason (problem) and the impact of the different ending (solution).

LS.2.7.10 Recount experiences or present stories that: move through a logical sequence of events; describe story elements, including characters, plot, and setting.

Page 93 • Vowels *aw, au, augh, al*

RD.2.1.1 Demonstrate an awareness of the sounds that are made by different letters by: distinguishing beginning, middle, and ending sounds in words; rhyming words; clearly pronouncing blends and vowel sounds.

WR.2.6.9 Spell correctly words with short- and long-vowel sounds (*a, e, i, o, u*), *r*-controlled vowels (*ar, er, ir, or, ur*), and consonant-blend patterns (*bl, dr, st*).

Page 94 • Realism and Fantasy

RD.2.2.2 State the purpose for reading.

RD.2.3.4.1 Recognize the difference between fantasy and reality.

Day Two

Page 95 • Realism and Fantasy

RD.2.2.2 State the purpose for reading.

RD.2.3.4.1 Recognize the difference between fantasy and reality.

Page 96 • Lesson Vocabulary

RD.2.1.8 Use knowledge of individual words to predict the meaning of unknown compound words (*lunchtime, lunchroom, daydream, raindrop*).

RD.2.1.10 Identify simple multiple-meaning words (*change, duck*).

WR.2.6.8 Spell correctly words like *was, were, says, said, who, what,* and *why,* which are used frequently but do not fit common spelling patterns.

Page 97 • Author's Purpose

RD.2.2.3 Use knowledge of the author's purpose(s) to comprehend informational text.

RD.2.3.4.3 Understand or interpret what is read or heard by responding to questions (*who, what, when, where, why, how*) and by using appropriate comprehension strategies, such as drawing conclusions, identifying the author's purpose, relating to prior knowledge, restating details, or setting a purpose for reading.

Day Three

Page 98 • *ph, gh/f/*

RD.2.1.3 Decode (sound out) regular words with more than one syllable (*dinosaur, vacation*).

WR.2.6.8 Spell correctly words like *was, were, says, said, who, what,* and *why,* which are used frequently but do not fit common spelling patterns.

Page 99 • Lesson Vocabulary

RD.2.1.2 Recognize and use knowledge of spelling patterns (such as *cut/cutting, slide/sliding*) when reading.

RD.2.1.5 Identify and correctly use regular plural words (*mountain/mountains*) and irregular plural words (*child/children, mouse/mice*).

WR.2.6.8 Spell correctly words like *was, were, says, said, who, what,* and *why,* which are used frequently but do not fit common spelling patterns.

Day Five

Page 100 • Online Sources

WR.2.4.5 Use a computer to draft, revise, and publish writing.

LS.2.7.11 Report on a topic with facts and details, drawing from several sources of information.

Unit 6 • **Just Like Josh Gibson**

Day One

Pages 101–102 • Family Times

RD.2.2.5 Restate facts and details or summarize the main idea in the text to clarify and organize ideas.

LS.2.7.7 Tell experiences in a logical order.

LS.2.7.9 Report on a topic with supportive facts and details.

Page 103 • Contractions

RD.2.1.2 Recognize and use knowledge of spelling patterns (such as *cut/cutting, slide/sliding*) when reading.

RD.2.1.3 Decode (sound out) regular words with more than one syllable (*dinosaur, vacation*).

WR.2.6.8 Spell correctly words like *was, were, says, said, who, what,* and *why,* which are used frequently but do not fit common spelling patterns.

Page 104 • Compare and Contrast

RD.2.2.5 Restate facts and details or summarize the main idea in the text to clarify and organize ideas.

RD.2.2.6 Recognize cause-and-effect relationships in a text.

LS.2.7.9 Report on a topic with supportive facts and details.

Day Two

Page 105 • Compare and Contrast

RD.2.2.5 Restate facts and details or summarize the main idea in the text to clarify and organize ideas.

RD.2.2.6 Recognize cause-and-effect relationships in a text.

LS.2.7.9 Report on a topic with supportive facts and details.

Page 106 • Lesson Vocabulary

RD.2.1.2 Recognize and use knowledge of spelling patterns (such as *cut/cutting, slide/sliding*) when reading.

RD.2.1.3 Decode (sound out) regular words with more than one syllable (*dinosaur, vacation*).

RD.2.1.7 Understand and explain common synonyms (words with the same meaning) and antonyms (words with opposite meanings).

Page 107 • Fact and Opinion

RD.2.2.3 Use knowledge of the author's purpose(s) to comprehend informational text.

RD.2.2.4 Ask and respond to questions (*why, what if, how*) to aid comprehension about important elements of informational texts.

LS.2.7.9 Report on a topic with supportive facts and details.

Day Three

Page 108 • Vowels *aw, au, augh, al*

RD.2.1.3 Decode (sound out) regular words with more than one syllable (*dinosaur, vacation*).

WR.2.6.8 Spell correctly words like *was, were, says, said, who, what,* and *why,* which are used frequently but do not fit common spelling patterns.

Page 109 • Lesson Vocabulary

RD.2.1.2 Recognize and use knowledge of spelling patterns (such as *cut/cutting, slide/sliding*) when reading.

RD.2.1.5 Identify and correctly use regular plural words (*mountain/mountains*) and irregular plural words (*child/children, mouse/mice*).

RD.2.1.7 Understand and explain common synonyms (words with the same meaning) and antonyms (words with opposite meanings).

Day Five

Page 110 • People as Resources

LS.2.7.3 Paraphrase (restate in own words) information that has been shared orally by others.

LS.2.7.11 Report on a topic with facts and details, drawing from several sources of information.

Unit 6 • **Red, White, and Blue: The Story of the American Flag**

Day One

Pages 111–112 • Family Times

RD.2.2.5 Restate facts and details or summarize the main idea in the text to clarify and organize ideas.

LS.2.7.7 Tell experiences in a logical order.

LS.2.7.9 Report on a topic with supportive facts and details.

Page 113 • Inflected Endings

RD.2.1.2 Recognize and use knowledge of spelling patterns (such as *cut/cutting, slide/sliding*) when reading.

RD.2.1.8.1 Read and understand more difficult root words (such as *chase*) and their inflectional forms (*chases, chased, chasing*).

Page 114 • Fact and Opinion

RD.2.2.3 Use knowledge of the author's purpose(s) to comprehend informational text.

RD.2.2.4 Ask and respond to questions (*why, what if, how*) to aid comprehension about important elements of informational texts.

LS.2.7.9 Report on a topic with supportive facts and details.

Day Two

Page 115 • Fact and Opinion

RD.2.2.3 Use knowledge of the author's purpose(s) to comprehend informational text.

RD.2.2.4 Ask and respond to questions (*why, what if, how*) to aid comprehension about important elements of informational texts.

RD.2.2.5 Restate facts and details or summarize the main idea in the text to clarify and organize ideas.

Page 116 • Lesson Vocabulary

RD.2.1.2 Recognize and use knowledge of spelling patterns (such as *cut/cutting, slide/sliding*) when reading.

RD.2.1.6 Read aloud fluently and accurately with appropriate changes in voice and expression.

RD.2.1.7 Understand and explain common synonyms (words with the same meaning) and antonyms (words with opposite meanings).

Page 117 • Main Idea

RD.2.2.3 Use knowledge of the author's purpose(s) to comprehend informational text.

RD.2.2.4 Ask and respond to questions (*why, what if, how*) to aid comprehension about important elements of informational texts.

RD.2.2.5 Restate facts and details or summarize the main idea in the text to clarify and organize ideas.

Day Three

Page 118 • Contractions

RD.2.1.2 Recognize and use knowledge of spelling patterns (such as *cut/cutting, slide/sliding*) when reading.

WR.2.6.8 Spell correctly words like *was, were, says, said, who, what,* and *why,* which are used frequently but do not fit common spelling patterns.

Page 119 • Lesson Vocabulary

RD.2.1.2 Recognize and use knowledge of spelling patterns (such as *cut/cutting, slide/sliding*) when reading.

RD.2.1.7 Understand and explain common synonyms (words with the same meaning) and antonyms (words with opposite meanings).

RD.2.1.10 Identify simple multiple-meaning words (*change, duck*).

Day Five

Page 120 • Take Notes/Outline

WR.2.4.1 Create a list of ideas for writing.

WR.2.4.2 Organize related ideas together to maintain a consistent focus.

Unit 6 • A Birthday Basket for Tía

Day One

Pages 121–122 • Family Times

LS.2.7.7 Tell experiences in a logical order.

LS.2.7.8 Retell stories, including characters, setting, and plot.

LS.2.7.9 Report on a topic with supportive facts and details.

Page 123 • Syllables *-tion, -ture*

RD.2.1.2 Recognize and use knowledge of spelling patterns (such as *cut/cutting, slide/sliding*) when reading.

RD.2.1.3 Decode (sound out) regular words with more than one syllable (*dinosaur, vacation*).

WR.2.6.8 Spell correctly words like *was, were, says, said, who, what,* and *why,* which are used frequently but do not fit common spelling patterns.

Page 124 • Draw Conclusions

RD.2.2.8.1 Understand or interpret what is read or heard by continuing to use comprehension strategies such as those involving context, drawing conclusions, or prior knowledge.

RD.2.3.4.3 Understand or interpret what is read or heard by responding to questions (*who, what, when, where, why, how*) and by using appropriate comprehension strategies, such as drawing conclusions, identifying the author's purpose, relating to prior knowledge, restating details, or setting a purpose for reading.

Day Two

Page 125 • Draw Conclusions

RD.2.2.8.1 Understand or interpret what is read or heard by continuing to use comprehension strategies such as those involving context, drawing conclusions, or prior knowledge.

RD.2.3.4.3 Understand or interpret what is read or heard by responding to questions (*who, what, when, where, why, how*) and by using appropriate comprehension strategies, such as drawing conclusions, identifying the author's purpose, relating to prior knowledge, restating details, or setting a purpose for reading.

Page 126 • Lesson Vocabulary

RD.2.1.3 Decode (sound out) regular words with more than one syllable (*dinosaur, vacation*).

RD.2.1.5 Identify and correctly use regular plural words (*mountain/mountains*) and irregular plural words (*child/children, mouse/mice*).

RD.2.1.10 Identify simple multiple-meaning words (*change, duck*).

Page 127 • Cause and Effect

RD.2.2.5 Restate facts and details or summarize the main idea in the text to clarify and organize ideas.

RD.2.2.6 Recognize cause-and-effect relationships in a text.

LS.2.7.8 Retell stories, including characters, setting, and plot.

Day Three

Page 128 • Inflected Endings

RD.2.1.2 Recognize and use knowledge of spelling patterns (such as *cut/cutting, slide/sliding*) when reading.

RD.2.1.8.1 Read and understand more difficult root words (such as *chase*) and their inflectional forms (*chases, chased, chasing*).

Page 129 • Lesson Vocabulary

RD.2.1.6 Read aloud fluently and accurately with appropriate changes in voice and expression.

RD.2.1.7 Understand and explain common synonyms (words with the same meaning) and antonyms (words with opposite meanings).

RD.2.1.8 Use knowledge of individual words to predict the meaning of unknown compound words (*lunchtime, lunchroom, daydream, raindrop*).

Day Five

Page 130 • Online Directories

WR.2.4.4 Understand the purposes of various reference materials (such as a dictionary, thesaurus, or atlas).

WR.2.4.5 Use a computer to draft, revise, and publish writing.

Unit 6 • Cowboys

Day One

Pages 131–132 • Family Times

LS.2.7.7 Tell experiences in a logical order.

LS.2.7.8 Retell stories, including characters, setting, and plot.

LS.2.7.9 Report on a topic with supportive facts and details.

Page 133 • Suffixes

RD.2.1.2 Recognize and use knowledge of spelling patterns (such as *cut/cutting, slide/sliding*) when reading.

RD.2.1.3 Decode (sound out) regular words with more than one syllable (*dinosaur, vacation*).

RD.2.1.9 Know the meaning of simple prefixes (word parts added at the beginning of words such as *un-*) and suffixes (word parts added at the end of words such as *-ful*).

Page 134 • Cause and Effect

RD.2.2.5 Restate facts and details or summarize the main idea in the text to clarify and organize ideas.

RD.2.2.6 Recognize cause-and-effect relationships in a text.

LS.2.7.10 Recount experiences or present stories that: move through a logical sequence of events; describe story elements, including characters, plot, and setting.

Day Two

Page 135 • Cause and Effect

RD.2.2.5 Restate facts and details or summarize the main idea in the text to clarify and organize ideas.

RD.2.2.6 Recognize cause-and-effect relationships in a text.

LS.2.7.8 Retell stories, including characters, setting, and plot.

Page 136 • Lesson Vocabulary

RD.2.1.3 Decode (sound out) regular words with more than one syllable (*dinosaur, vacation*).

RD.2.1.5 Identify and correctly use regular plural words (*mountain/mountains*) and irregular plural words (*child/children, mouse/mice*).

RD.2.1.10 Identify simple multiple-meaning words (*change, duck*).

Page 137 • Fact and Opinion

RD.2.2.3 Use knowledge of the author's purpose(s) to comprehend informational text.

RD.2.2.4 Ask and respond to questions (*why, what if, how*) to aid comprehension about important elements of informational texts.

LS.2.7.9 Report on a topic with supportive facts and details.

Day Three

Page 138 • Syllables *-tion, -ture*

RD.2.1.2 Recognize and use knowledge of spelling patterns (such as *cut/cutting, slide/sliding*) when reading.

RD.2.1.3 Decode (sound out) regular words with more than one syllable (*dinosaur, vacation*).

WR.2.6.8 Spell correctly words like *was, were, says, said, who, what,* and *why,* which are used frequently but do not fit common spelling patterns.

Page 139 • Lesson Vocabulary

RD.2.1.6 Read aloud fluently and accurately with appropriate changes in voice and expression.

RD.2.1.7 Understand and explain common synonyms (words with the same meaning) and antonyms (words with opposite meanings).

RD.2.1.8 Use knowledge of individual words to predict the meaning of unknown compound words (*lunchtime, lunchroom, daydream, raindrop*).

Day Five

Page 140 • Thesaurus

WR.2.4.4 Understand the purposes of various reference materials (such as a dictionary, thesaurus, or atlas).

LS.2.7.11 Report on a topic with facts and details, drawing from several sources of information.

Unit 6 • Jingle Dancer

Day One

Pages 141–142 • Family Times

RD.2.2.6 Recognize cause-and-effect relationships in a text.

LS.2.7.8 Retell stories, including characters, setting, and plot.

LS.2.7.10 Recount experiences or present stories that: move through a logical sequence of events; describe story elements, including characters, plot, and setting.

Page 143 • Prefixes

RD.2.1.2 Recognize and use knowledge of spelling patterns (such as *cut/cutting, slide/sliding*) when reading.

RD.2.1.3 Decode (sound out) regular words with more than one syllable (*dinosaur, vacation*).

RD.2.1.9 Know the meaning of simple prefixes (word parts added at the beginning of words such as *un-*) and suffixes (word parts added at the end of words such as *-ful*).

Page 144 • Character, Setting, Plot

RD.2.2.6 Recognize cause-and-effect relationships in a text.

LS.2.7.8 Retell stories, including characters, setting, and plot.

LS.2.7.10 Recount experiences or present stories that: move through a logical sequence of events; describe story elements, including characters, plot, and setting.

Day Two

Page 145 • Character, Setting, Plot

RD.2.3.1 Compare plots, settings, and characters presented by different authors.

LS.2.7.8 Retell stories, including characters, setting, and plot.

LS.2.7.10 Recount experiences or present stories that: move through a logical sequence of events; describe story elements, including characters, plot, and setting.

Page 146 • Lesson Vocabulary

RD.2.1.2 Recognize and use knowledge of spelling patterns (such as *cut/cutting, slide/sliding*) when reading.

RD.2.1.10 Identify simple multiple-meaning words (*change, duck*).

WR.2.4.4 Understand the purposes of various reference materials (such as a dictionary, thesaurus, or atlas).

Page 147 • Cause and Effect

RD.2.2.5 Restate facts and details or summarize the main idea in the text to clarify and organize ideas.

RD.2.2.6 Recognize cause-and-effect relationships in a text.

LS.2.7.8 Retell stories, including characters, setting, and plot.

Day Three

Page 148 • Suffixes *-ness, -less*

RD.2.1.2 Recognize and use knowledge of spelling patterns (such as *cut/cutting, slide/sliding*) when reading.

RD.2.1.3 Decode (sound out) regular words with more than one syllable (*dinosaur, vacation*).

RD.2.1.9 Know the meaning of simple prefixes (word parts added at the beginning of words such as *un-*) and suffixes (word parts added at the end of words such as *-ful*).

Page 149 • Lesson Vocabulary

RD.2.1.2 Recognize and use knowledge of spelling patterns (such as *cut/cutting, slide/sliding*) when reading.

RD.2.1.3 Decode (sound out) regular words with more than one syllable (*dinosaur, vacation*).

WR.2.4.4 Understand the purposes of various reference materials (such as a dictionary, thesaurus, or atlas).

Day Five

Page 150 • Time Line

RD.2.2.7 Interpret information from diagrams, charts, and graphs.

WR.2.4.3 Find ideas for writing stories and descriptions in pictures or books.

Grade **2.2**

Scott Foresman
Practice Book

Editorial Offices: Glenview, Illinois • Parsippany, New Jersey • New York, New York
Sales Offices: Needham, Massachusetts • Duluth, Georgia • Glenview, Illinois
Coppell, Texas • Sacramento, California • Mesa, Arizona

ISBN: 0-328-14518-1

Copyright © Pearson Education, Inc.

All Rights Reserved. Printed in the United States of America. The blackline masters in this publication are designed for use with appropriate equipment to reproduce copies for classroom use only. Scott Foresman grants permission to classroom teachers to reproduce from these masters.

9 10 V004 11 10 09

Contents

Unit 6
Traditions

	Family Times	Phonics	Comprehension Skills	Vocabulary	Comprehension Review	Phonics Review	Research and Study Skills
Josh Gibson	101–102	103	104, 105	106, 109	107	108	110
Red, White, and Blue	111–112	113	114, 115	116, 119	117	118	120
Birthday Basket for Tía	121–122	123	124, 125	126, 129	127	128	130
Cowboys	131–132	133	134, 135	136, 139	137	138	140
Jingle Dancer	141–142	143	144, 145	146, 149	147	148	150

Family Times

Name

You are your child's first and best teacher!

This week we're

Reading The Quilt Story

Talking About How familiar things can help us with changes

Learning About Syllables C + *le*
Compare and Contrast

© Pearson Education 2

Here are ways to help your child practice skills while having fun!

Day 1

Have your child read these words: *bugle, cable, lumber, middle, planet, riddle, wrinkle.* Ask which words end with the sound made by -*le*, as in the last syllable of *apple.*

Day 2

Your child has been comparing and contrasting information in a reading passage. As you read aloud, ask your child to compare and contrast characters or events.

Day 3

Have your child read these words: *blankets, pretended, quilt, stuffing, trunks, unpacked, wrapped.* Ask your child the meaning of each word.

Day 4

Have your child write these spelling words: *able, ankle, apple, bubble, bugle, bundle, cable, giggle, purple, sparkle, tickle, title.* Work together to make up story titles with these words.

Day 5

This week your child has been learning to write descriptions. Have your child write a paragraph that compares and contrasts two rooms in your home. Help your child draw the rooms.

Same or Different?

Materials index cards, crayons or markers

Game Directions

1. Use index cards to make a set of pictures as shown.

2. Mix the pictures and spread them face down.

3. Players take turns turning over two pictures and trying to make a match.

4. If a match is made, the player tells how the pictures are alike and different and keeps the pair. If no match is made, the player places the pictures face down where they were.

5. Play continues until all pairs are matched.

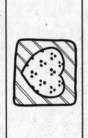

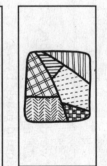

© Pearson Education 2

Name _____

ankle   bubble   bugle   people   table   turtle

Say the word for each picture.
Write the word on the line.
Use the words in the box if you need help.

 app**le**

1.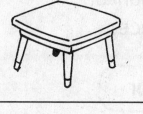
_____
- - - - - - - - - -

2.
_____
- - - - - - - - - -

3.
_____
- - - - - - - - - -

4.
_____
- - - - - - - - - -

5.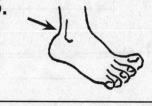
_____
- - - - - - - - - -

6.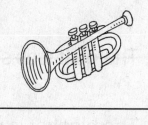
_____
- - - - - - - - - -

Find the picture that ends with the same sound as the last syllable in **able**. **Mark** the space to show your answer.

7. ⬭    ⬭    ⬭

8. ⬭   ⬭    ⬭

 School + Home   **Home Activity** Your child wrote words that end in *le* and have more than one syllable, such as *apple*. Have your child make word cards for *le* words, such as those above. Ask your child to write the word on the front of the card and draw a picture of it on the back of the card.

© Pearson Education 2

Name _____

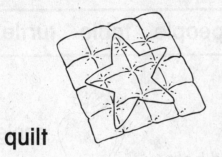

quilt

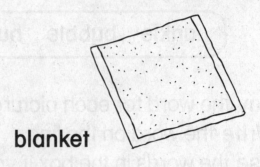

blanket

Look for ways in which the quilt is not like the blanket.
Write a word from the box to finish each sentence.

needle   one   scraps   star

_____

1. The quilt is made of _____ of cloth.

2. The quilt was sewn with a _____ and thread.

3. The blanket is made from _____ piece of cloth.

4. The blanket does not have a _____ .

5. Write a sentence that tells how these two things are alike.

_____

_____

_____

_____

Home Activity Your child described ways in which two things are similar and different. Together, compare some of the blankets or comforters you have at home. Ask your child to describe specific differences and similarities between the blankets.

© Pearson Education 2

Name _____

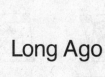 Long Ago  | Today

Look for ways in which the bedroom from long ago is **not** like today's bedroom.

Write two sentences about the bedroom from long ago.

1. _____

_____

2. _____

Write one sentence that tells how these two bedrooms are alike.

3. _____

Look for ways in which today's bedroom is **not** like the bedroom from long ago.

Write two sentences about today's bedroom.

4. _____

_____

5. _____

Home Activity Your child described ways in which bedrooms from different times are the same and different. Together, compare family photos of houses or rooms from earlier generations. Ask your child to describe what is the same and different about those places.

© Pearson Education 2

Name _____

Write a word to finish each sentence.

> blankets pretended quilt stuffing
> trunks unpacked wrapped

1. My mom and I are stitching a _____ .

2. Mom _____ her needles and thread.

3. I _____ myself with a shawl to stay warm.

4. The quilt is filled with _____ to make it warm.

5. My little sister _____ to make a quilt.

6. Mom will store this quilt with the _____ .

7. We have two _____ for storing quilts.

 Home Activity Your child completed sentences using vocabulary words learned this week. Together, look at a quilt or blanket in your home. Ask your child to use some of these words to tell a story about a quilt or blanket.

© Pearson Education 2

Name _____

Read each part of the story.
Underline the sentence that tells where the story takes place.
Draw a picture of that place.

1. I sat inside our wagon. Mother told me to pack all my things. We would soon come to our new home! This wagon has been my home for many weeks.

2.

3. I brought my trunk into my new room. The room is so big! It has a window too. I can't wait to unpack my toys. I love my new room.

4.

Write a sentence that tells about the character in this story.
Draw a picture of the character.

5. _____

_____

_____

_____

Home Activity Your child identified the setting and described a character in a story. Select several older family photos that show family members in earlier times. Together with your child, describe what can be seen of the different settings in the pictures.

© Pearson Education 2

Name _____

Spot is big.
Rover is bigger.
Spike is biggest.

Circle a word to finish each sentence.

1. I went to the (bigger / biggest) party
   I've ever seen.

2. It was for Jack, the (older / oldest) of all the children.

3. I am five years (younger / youngest) than he is.

4. Jack was the (hungrier / hungriest) person at the party.

5. He ate the (larger / largest) piece of cake.

Write a word from the box to finish each sentence.

> busier   hottest   tallest

6. Today is the _____ day of the year.

7. The swimming pool is _____ than ever.

8. I jumped off the _____ diving board.

Home Activity Your child reviewed, identified, and wrote words that end with *-er (bigger)* and *-est (biggest)*.
Name items your child can compare, such as pieces of fruit or items of clothing. Help your child write
sentences using words such as *larger, largest, smaller,* and *smallest* to compare each group of items.

© Pearson Education 2

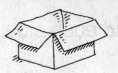

Name _____

Pick a word from the box to match each clue.
Write the letters of the word in each puzzle.

> blankets pretended quilt stuffing
> trunks unpacked wrapped

1. bed cover made of patches

   1. ☐ ☐ ☐ ☐ ☐

2. large suitcases

   2. ☐ ☐ ☐ ☐ ☐ ☐

3. put paper around

   3. ☐ ☐ ☐ ☐ ☐ ☐ ☐

4. filling

   4. ☐ ☐ ☐ ☐ ☐ ☐ ☐ ☐

5. bed clothes
   without patches

   5. ☐ ☐ ☐ ☐ ☐ ☐ ☐ ☐

6. took things
   out of boxes

   6. ☐ ☐ ☐ ☐ ☐ ☐ ☐ ☐

7. played
   make-believe

   7. ☐ ☐ ☐ ☐ ☐ ☐ ☐ ☐ ☐

Home Activity Your child used clues to write vocabulary words learned this week. Work with your child to use some of this week's vocabulary words to write a story about packing and moving.

© Pearson Education 2

Name _____

Read each clue. **Circle** the picture that best fits each clue.

1. It tells what words mean and how to say them.

2. It has many kinds of maps.

3. It gives today's news.

4. It lists words with nearly the same meanings.

5. It has facts about quilts.

 Home Activity Your child learned about print and media reference sources. Choose a topic you and your child would like to learn more about. Talk about the types of reference sources you could use to learn more. Go to the library to find some of the sources.

© Pearson Education 2

Family Times

© Pearson Education 2

Name

You are your child's first and best teacher!

This week we're

Reading Life Cycle of a Pumpkin

Life Cycle of a Pumpkin
by Ron Fridell and Patricia Walsh

How does a pumpkin go from seed to pie?

Expository nonfiction tells facts about a topic. Look for facts about how a pumpkin grows.

Talking About How plants change as they grow

Learning About Vowels *oo, u*
Fact and Opinion

Here are ways to help your child practice skills while having fun!

 Day 1

Have your child read these words: *brook, full, wood.* Ask your child to name two words that rhyme with each word on the list.

 Day 2

Your child has been identifying statements of fact and opinion. As you read aloud a nonfiction selection, ask your child to identify statements of fact and opinion.

 Day 3

Have your child read these words: *bumpy, fruit, harvest, root, smooth, soil, vine.* Work together to use the words in a silly song. Write the song lyrics and ask your child to read them.

 Day 4

Have your child write these spelling words: *brook, cook, full, hood, hook, July, pull, push, put, shook, stood, wood.* Cut apart each word into letters. Have your child put the letters back together to correctly spell each word.

 Day 5

This week your child has been reading about plants and identifying statements of fact and opinion. Ask what your child has learned. Have your child write at least three statements of fact and three statements of opinion about plants.

Materials coin, two buttons

Game Directions

1. Players place buttons at Start.
2. Players take turns flipping a coin and moving one space for heads and two spaces for tails.
3. When a player lands on a word, he or she reads the word and tells whether or not it has the vowel sound in *book*. Players who fail to correctly read the word and identify the vowel sound move back one space.
4. Play continues until all players reach the end.

2

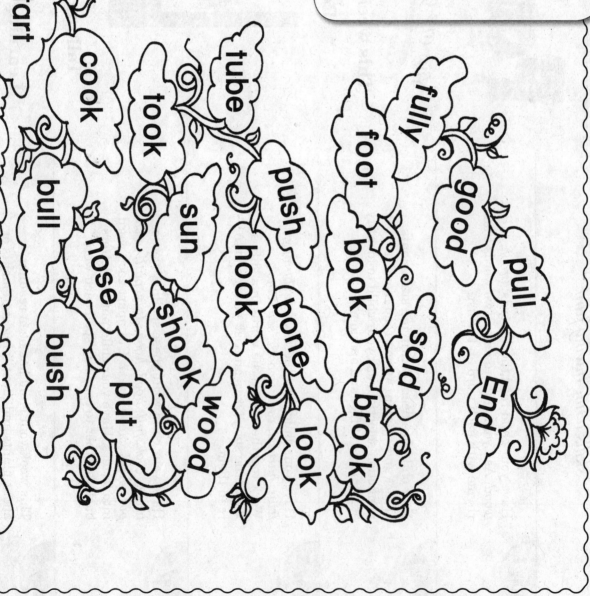

3

© Pearson Education 2

Name _____

 c**oo**k

 b**u**ll

| full hood hook pull shook stood took wood |

Write three words from the box that rhyme with **good**.

1. _____ 2. _____ 3. _____

Write three words from the box that rhyme with **look**.

4. _____ 5. _____ 6. _____

Write a word from the box that is the opposite of each word below.

7. push 8. empty

_____ _____

_____

Write a word from the box to finish each sentence.

| brook   put |

9. I _____ a hook on the fishing pole.

10. I pulled a fish from the _____ .

 School + Home **Home Activity** Your child wrote words that have the vowel sound in *cook*, spelled *oo* and *u* as in *bull*. Help your child write a rhyming poem using words with the vowel sound in *cook*. The poem can be silly or serious. Encourage your child to illustrate the poem and read it aloud.

© Pearson Education 2

Name _____

Write F before each sentence that gives a **fact**.
Write O before each sentence that gives an **opinion**.
Underline clue words such as **best, good, should,** or **beautiful**.

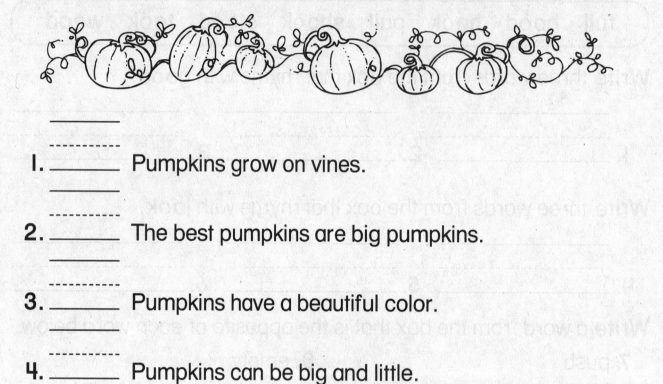

1. _____ Pumpkins grow on vines.

2. _____ The best pumpkins are big pumpkins.

3. _____ Pumpkins have a beautiful color.

4. _____ Pumpkins can be big and little.

Mark the spaces to show your answers.

5. Which sentence is a **fact**?

- ⬭ Everyone should grow pumpkins.
- ⬭ Pumpkin seeds taste good.
- ⬭ Pumpkins can be different sizes.

6. Which sentence is an **opinion**?

- ⬭ Pumpkins can grow big.
- ⬭ I grew the best pumpkin.
- ⬭ Baby pumpkins are green.

© Pearson Education 2

 Home Activity Your child learned the difference between facts (statements that can be proved true or false) and opinions (statements that express a feeling or belief). Together, read an easy article from the newspaper or a magazine. As you read, ask your child to point out statements that are facts and opinions.

Name _____

Read the story. **Underline** the sentences that are **opinions**.
Circle the clue words. **Answer** each question.

My name is Steve. This summer I planted my first garden.
It is the best garden on the block. I planted peppers and pumpkins.
I water my plants a lot. I think my pumpkin is the nicest
one in town. The pumpkin contest is coming soon. I'm sure
I will win first prize!

_____

I. **Write** one sentence from the story that is a **fact**.

_____

_____

_____

2. **Write** one sentence from the story that is an **opinion**.

_____

_____

_____

© Pearson Education 2

Home Activity Your child showed which sentences were statements of fact or opinion. Select a favorite book. As you read the book together, ask your child to point out statements that are facts and opinions.

Name _____

Write a word from the box to finish each sentence.

> bumpy   fruit   harvest   root   smooth   soil   vine

1. Make sure you plant your tree in good _____ .

2. Water it so it will take _____ in the soil.

3. The bark on the tree may be _____ .

4. Make sure the _____ is ripe before you pick it.

5. Apples do not grow on a _____ .

6. You can _____ apples in the fall.

7. An apple peel feels _____ .

© Pearson Education 2

Home Activity Your child completed sentences using vocabulary words learned this week. Together, prepare a snack or dessert using apples. As you work, ask your child to use these vocabulary words to describe how apples are grown.

Name _____

 pumpkin apple

Look for ways in which the pumpkin is **not** like the apple.
Write one sentence about the pumpkin.

1. _____

Write one sentence that tells how both fruits are alike.

2. _____

Look for ways in which the apple is **not** like the pumpkin.
Write one sentence about the apple.

3. _____

 Home Activity Your child described ways in which two things are alike and different. Take your child to the grocery store or produce stand to look at fruits and vegetables. Encourage your child to describe the similarities and differences among produce you see.

© Pearson Education 2

Name _____

Pick a word from the box to match each clue.
Write the word on the line.

 apple

> bundle   eagle   fable   gentle
> marble   purple   sparkle   title

1. a name given to a book or song _____

2. a color mixed from red and blue _____

3. a package _____

4. to shine _____

5. a story that teaches a lesson _____

6. a small, glass ball _____

7. a very big bird _____

8. soft and mild _____

© Pearson Education 2

 School + Home **Home Activity** Your child reviewed words that end with *-le* and have more than one syllable, such as *apple*. Work with your child to write a poem or story using some of the *-le* words shown above. Ask your child to read aloud his or her finished writing.

Name _____

Read the story. **Pick** a word from the box to finish each sentence. **Write** the word on the line.

| bumpy   fruit   harvest   root   smooth   soil   vine |

The Life of a Pumpkin

Most pumpkins look like sleek, _____, round heads.

Pumpkins begin when the seeds are planted in the

_____   _____ . Then they sprout and _____ in the

ground. Baby pumpkins will grow on a long _____ .

Soon they are bigger than any _____. They look like

little suns. Their stems are hard and _____.

Then comes the pumpkin _____ . After the pumpkins

are picked, the vines are turned back into the soil. The pumpkin's

life will start again next year.

Home Activity Your child completed sentences in a story using vocabulary words learned this week. Together, visit a local pumpkin patch or plant pumpkin seeds in a planter or in your yard. Ask your child to use these vocabulary words to describe the pumpkins on the vine.

© Pearson Education 2

Name _____

Look at the circle graph. **Write** the answer to each question.

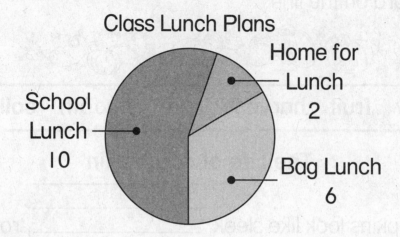

Class Lunch Plans

Home for
Lunch
2

School
Lunch
10

Bag Lunch
6

1. What does the graph show?

_____

- -

_____

- -

_____

2. How many children have a bag lunch? _____

3. How many children are getting the school lunch? _____

4. How many more children are eating at school than are going

home? _____

5. How many children are there in all? _____

Home Activity Your child learned how to read a circle graph. Help your child make a circle graph to show how a group or collection is divided. For example, the chart can show how many white socks there are in the drawer, how many black socks, how many blue socks, and so forth.

© Pearson Education 2

© Pearson Education 2

Family Times

You are your child's first and best teacher!

Name _____

This week we're

Reading Frogs

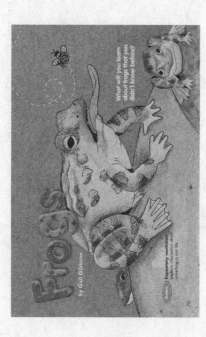

Frogs
by Gail Gibbons

What will you learn about frogs that you didn't know before?

70

Talking About How animals change as they grow

Learning About Diphthongs ou, ow/ou/
Compare and Contrast

Here are ways to help your child practice skills while having fun!

Day 1
Have your child read these words aloud: *about, flower, mouth, prowl, round, town.* Ask which letters spell the vowel sound /ou/, as in *found* and *gown.*

Day 2
Your child has been learning to compare and contrast. Read aloud two short poems or songs. Ask how they are alike and different.

Day 3
Have your child read these words: *crawls, insects, pond, powerful, shed, skin, wonderful.* Write sentences with these words, but leave a blank for each listed word. Have your child write the word that completes each sentence.

Day 4
Have your child write these spelling words: *about, around, crown, downtown, flower, gown, ground, howl, mouse, pound, sound, south.* Together, make up two-line rhymes for each word.

Day 5
This week your child has been comparing and contrasting animals. Have your child write a paragraph to compare and contrast two types of pets.

Materials white paper, scissors, paper clip, pencils, index cards

Game Directions

1. Make a simple spinner as shown. Use index cards to make word cards as shown.

2. Mix the word cards and divide the cards among players.

3. Players take turns spinning and checking their cards for a word with that letter pair. If a match is found, that player reads the word and removes it from his or her hand.

4. Play continues until all words have been matched with a letter pair.

ou
ow

about	around	brown	cloud
clown	cow	crown	down
flower	frown	ground	house
how	howl	loud	mouse
pound	sound	south	town

© Pearson Education 2

Name _____

Read each sentence.
Circle the word with the same vowel sound as **cow** or **house**.
Write the word on the line.

cow   house

1. I play baseball near my house. _____

2. We are the best team in town. _____

3. We are the Brown Bears. _____

4. We play about once a week. _____

5. I went downtown to the park. _____

6. There wasn't a cloud in the sky. _____

7. The crowd was cheering. _____

8. My teammates shouted too. _____

9. I hit a ground ball. _____

Home Activity Your child wrote words that have the vowel sound in *gown*, spelled *ow* as in *cow* and *ou* as in *house*. Ask your child to draw pictures representing words with the vowel sound in *gown*, such as *mouse*, *crown*, *flower*, *frown*, and *loud*. Work together to label each picture.

© Pearson Education 2

Name _____

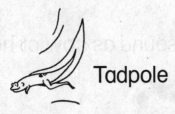 Tadpole

 Frog

A tadpole is a baby frog.

Look for ways in which the tadpole does **not** look like the frog.

Write one sentence about the tadpole.

1. _____

Write one sentence that tells how the tadpole and frog are alike.

2. _____

Look for ways in which the frog does **not** look like the tadpole.

Write one sentence about the frog.

3. _____

© Pearson Education 2

School + Home **Home Activity** Your child described ways in which two things are the same and different. Together, look at picture books or magazines that show baby animals. Ask your child to describe specific ways that the babies are different from or similar to the adult animals.

24 **Comprehension** Compare and Contrast

Practice Book Unit 4

Name _____

 bug

 bird

Look for ways in which a bug is **not** like a bird.
Write a word to finish each sentence.

_____

1. A bug does not have a _____ .   wing   beak

2. A bug has _____ on its back.   spots   feathers

Look for ways in which a real bird is not like a real bug.
Write a word to finish each sentence.

3. A bird has _____ legs.   six   two

4. A bird is _____ in size.   smaller   larger

Write a sentence that tells how birds and bugs are alike.

_____
_____
_____
_____

© Pearson Education 2

 Home Activity Your child described ways in which two things are the same and different. Together, look at pictures of birds and insects. Ask your child to describe similarities and differences between them.

Name _____

Write a word to finish each sentence.

| crawls | insects | pond | powerful |
| shed | skin | wonderful | |

1. A snake's _____ is really smooth to touch.

2. Snakes _____ their skin as they grow.

3. A snake _____ along the ground.

4. Many snakes have _____ jaws. They also have large, sharp fangs.

5. Snakes can swim and sometimes live in a _____ .

6. Most _____ are too small for snakes to eat.

7. Snakes are _____ animals.

Home Activity Your child completed sentences using vocabulary words learned this week. Select a magazine article or Web site about snakes. Ask your child to look for these vocabulary words as they read.

© Pearson Education 2

Name _____

Read the sentences.

Think about which give **facts** and which give **opinions** about frogs and snakes.

Frogs eat many insects.   Snakes are fun to watch.
I believe frogs give you warts. Snakes eat small animals.
I don't like frogs.   Snakes live under rocks.

Write the sentences that give **facts**.

I. _____

_____

2. _____

_____

3. _____

Mark the spaces to show your answers.

4. Which is an **opinion**?   5. Which is a **fact**?

⬭ Frogs live near water.   ⬭ Snakes lay eggs.

⬭ Frogs have long legs.   ⬭ Snakes scare
                                     everyone.

⬭ Frogs are ugly.   ⬭ No one likes snakes.

Home Activity Your child decided which statements were facts and which were opinions. Visit a local nature center or zoo to observe snakes and frogs, or look at pictures of these animals. Discuss with your child the difference between facts and opinions about these two animals.

© Pearson Education 2

Name _____

Find the words from the box in the puzzle.
They may go across or down.
Circle each word in the puzzle.
Write the words on the lines.

cook   bull

book   bush   full   hook   put   stood

s	t	o	o	d	x	g	l	b	w
b	v	y	b	o	o	k	o	f	a
t	b	c	y	u	w	e	u	u	o
o	u	e	o	p	u	t	w	l	d
z	s	j	g	o	s	y	k	l	c
k	h	b	h	o	o	k	n	y	v

1. _____

2. _____

3. _____

4. _____

5. _____

6. _____

___

Find the word that has the same vowel sound as the picture.
Mark the space to show your answer.

7. ⬭ fun
   ⬭ fox
   ⬭ foot

8. ⬭ puppy
   ⬭ push
   ⬭ poke

Home Activity Your child reviewed words that have the vowel sound in *book*, spelled *oo* as in *cook* and *u* as in *bull*. Make a word search puzzle like the one above for your child to solve. Include words with the vowel sound in *book*, such as *hood, took, wood, push,* and *pull*.

© Pearson Education 2

Name _____

Pick a word from the box to match each clue.
Write the word on the line.

> crawls   insects   pond   powerful
> shed   skin   wonderful

1. bugs

_____

- - - - - - - - - - - - - - - -

_____

2. very good

_____

- - - - - - - - - - - - - - - -

_____

3. all over your body

_____

- - - - - - - - - - - - - - - -

_____

4. a small lake

_____

- - - - - - - - - - - - - - - -

_____

5. moves very slowly

_____

- - - - - - - - - - - - - - - -

_____

6. very strong

_____

- - - - - - - - - - - - - - - -

_____

7. to take off a layer

_____

- - - - - - - - - - - - - - - -

_____

© Pearson Education 2

Home Activity Your child used clues to identify and write vocabulary words learned this week. Check out from the library books on pond life. Encourage your child to look for these vocabulary words when reading about pond life.

Name _____

Use the diagram to answer the questions.

Goldfish

Scales protect the fish.

The goldfish has no **eyelids.**

Fins help the fish move.

Gills are used for breathing.

I. What does the diagram show?

_____

_____

2. What do the gills do?

_____

_____

3. What are fins for?

_____

_____

4. How are scales helpful?

_____

_____

5. Why are a goldfish's eyes always open?

_____

_____

School + Home

Home Activity Your child learned how to read a diagram. Look in a newspaper, magazine, or nonfiction book for a simple diagram. Discuss what the diagram shows. Help your child read the labels. Ask how the diagram helped your child better understand the subject.

© Pearson Education 2

Family Times

Name

You are your child's first and best teacher!

This week we're

Reading I Like Where I Am

Talking About Why some changes are difficult

Learning About Diphthongs *oi, oy*
Plot and Theme

© Pearson Education 2

Here are ways to help your child practice skills while having fun!

Day 1

Have your child read these words: *box, coil, destroy, grow, loyal, moist*. Ask your child to tell which words have the vowel sound in *joy*.

Day 2

Your child has been learning about plot and theme. Read a fairy tale together and ask what lesson your child learned. Ask what happened in the beginning, middle, and end of the story.

Day 3

Have your child read these words: *block, chuckle, fair, giant, strong, tears, trouble*. Have your child ask you questions using these words.

Day 4

Have your child write these spelling words on strips of paper: *broil, cowboy, destroy, enjoy, foil, joint, joy, loyal, moist, noise, royal, spoil*. Have your child sort the words by spelling pattern: words with *oy* and words with *oi*.

Day 5

This week your child has been summarizing text and reading about making changes. Ask your child to write a summary about a change that was hard to accept.

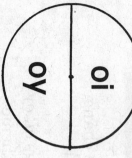

oi

oy

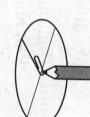

Materials white paper, scissors, paper clip, pencil, buttons

Game Directions

1. Make a simple spinner as shown.

2. Players take turns spinning a letter pair and tossing a button on the gameboard to try to land on a word that has the same letter pair. If a player fails to land on a word with the same letter pair, the play goes to the next person.

3. Play continues until all the words have been matched with a letter pair.

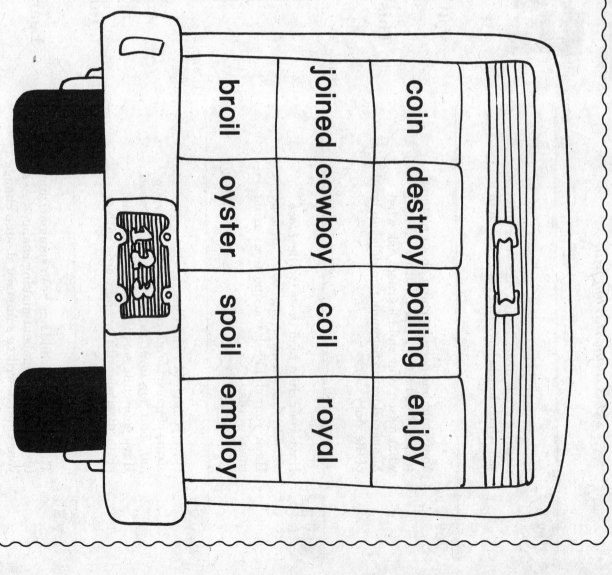

coin	destroy	boiling	enjoy
joined	cowboy	coil	royal
broil	oyster	spoil	employ

© Pearson Education 2

Name _____

b**oi**l

b**oy**

┌───┐
│ broil   coin   cowboy   enjoy   loyal   noise   point   voice │
└───┘

Write the word from the box that rhymes with each word below.

1. choice

_____

_____

2. toys

_____

_____

3. spoil

_____

_____

4. royal

_____

_____

Pick a word from the box to match each clue.

Write the word on the line.

5. a penny

_____

_____

6. the end of a sharp pencil

_____

_____

Pick a word from the box to finish each sentence.

Write the word on the line.

_____

7. I _____ movies.

_____

8. I like _____ stories best.

© Pearson Education 2

Home Activity Your child wrote words that have the vowel sound in *joy*, spelled *oi* as in *boil* and *oy* as in *toy*. Say a word from the box on the page above. Ask your child to use the word in a sentence. Repeat the word and have your child write it. Continue the activity with other words from the box.

Name _____

Read each story.
Answer the questions.

Joy's family was moving. First, Joy had to pack her clothes. Then she helped her mom pack towels. The last thing she did was pack her toys.

1. **Underline** the sentence that tells what Joy did first.

2. **Write** the sentence that tells what Joy did last.

_____

- -

_____

Joy was afraid about moving. Who would she play with? Would there be other children in the neighborhood? She helped her mom finish packing. Then the movers loaded everything onto the van. Her mom told her not to worry.

3. **Circle** the sentence that is the big idea of the story.

She helped her mom finish packing.

Joy was afraid about moving.

4. **Underline** one sentence of the story that helped you tell the big idea.

5. **Underline** another sentence of the story that helped you tell the big idea.

Home Activity Your child identified the order of story events and the big idea in a story. Together, select several storybooks from home or the library. As you read the stories, ask your child to identify the order of the story events and the big idea of each story.

© Pearson Education 2

Name _____

Read the story.
Answer the questions.

My brother and I loaded our clothes. Our family's robot lifted the beds and dressers. Everything went into the moving ship. My family is moving today. At last, we took off in our space jet. We were on our way to our new home. I hope there are some nice kids on Mars!

1. What happens at the beginning of this story?

_____

- -

_____

2. What happens at the end of this story?

_____

- -

_____

3. What is the big idea of this story—the family moves or the family packs?

_____

- -

_____

4. **Write** a title for this story.

_____

- -

_____

Home Activity Your child identified the order of story events and the big idea in a story. Together, write a plan for how your family would move. Ask your child to identify the steps you would take when moving. Then have your child write a sentence to tell the big idea of the plan.

Practice Book Unit 4

© Pearson Education 2

Comprehension Plot and Theme **35**

Name _____

Pick a word from the box to match each clue.
Write the word on the line.

---

block   chuckle   fair   giant   strong   tears   trouble

---

1. something big

   _____
   - - - - - - - - - - - - - - - - - -
   _____

2. able to lift heavy things

   _____
   - - - - - - - - - - - - - - - - - -
   _____

3. laugh softly

   _____
   - - - - - - - - - - - - - - - - - -
   _____

4. these come when you cry

   _____
   - - - - - - - - - - - - - - - - - -
   _____

5. a park with rides

   _____
   - - - - - - - - - - - - - - - - - -
   _____

6. something wrong

   _____
   - - - - - - - - - - - - - - - - - -
   _____

7. a cube of wood

   _____
   - - - - - - - - - - - - - - - - - -
   _____

Mark the space to show your answer.

8. What is another meaning of **block**?
   - ⬭ to read something
   - ⬭ to stop something
   - ⬭ to move something

9. What is another meaning of **fair**?
   - ⬭ pretty
   - ⬭ heavy
   - ⬭ funny

© Pearson Education 2

School + Home **Home Activity** Your child used clues to identify and write vocabulary words learned this week. Together, look up the words in a child's dictionary. As you read, ask your child to identify multiple meanings for some words.

Name _____

Read the story.
Follow the directions below.

Maggie and Jean stared out the window of the moving van. They were parked in front of a big building. "Where is our house?" asked Jean.

"Up there," said Mom. She pointed up at some windows. They went inside and up the stairs. The bedrooms were small.

But at least they didn't have to share, like back on the farm.

"We don't have a yard," said Maggie. "Where will I grow my green beans?"

"Maybe we can build window boxes," said Jean. "That would be fun!"

1. Where is the moving van parked? _____
_____

2. How do you think Maggie and Jean feel? _____
_____

3. Where do you think the new home is? _____
_____

4. **Write** a sentence telling whether you think the girls will like their new home and why or why not.

_____
_____
_____

5. **Draw** a picture of the girls' new home.

Home Activity Your child read a story and drew conclusions from information in the story. As you read stories together, stop occasionally and ask questions that have answers not stated in the story. For example, ask how characters feel or why they do certain things.

© Pearson Education 2

Name _____

Pick a word from the box to match each picture or clue.
Write the word on the line.

 h<u>ou</u>se    c<u>ow</u>

couch   downtown   flower   frown
ground   mouse   sound   south

1.

_____

_____

2.

_____

_____

3.

_____

_____

4.

_____

_____

5. not north

_____

_____

6. land

_____

_____

7. what you hear

_____

_____

8. opposite of smile

_____

_____

© Pearson Education 2

 School + Home **Home Activity** Your child reviewed words that have the vowel sound in *gown*, spelled *ow* as in *cow* and *ou* as in *house*. Have your child say words that rhyme with some of the *ou* and *ow* words on this page. Help your child write each pair of rhyming words.

Name _____

Pick a word from the box to finish each sentence.
Write the word on the line.

| block   chuckle   fair   giant   strong   tears   trouble |

_____
- - - - - - - - - - - - - - - - - - -
1. Joe was a _____. He was moving to a huge cave.

_____
- - - - - - - - - - - - - - - - - - -
2. Joe was happy to be moving. He gave a _____ as
he worked.

_____
- - - - - - - - - - - - - - - - - - -
3. Joe carried five tons of books. He was very _____.

_____
- - - - - - - - - - - - - - - - - - -
4. Joe stomped down the _____. He tripped and
almost fell on a house!

5. Then Joe tripped again and almost landed on some people

_____
- - - - - - - - - - - - - - - - - - -
at the town _____.

6. The people yelled at Joe. That made

_____
- - - - - - - - - - - - - - - - - - -
_____ come to his eyes.

7. Joe said there would be no

_____
- - - - - - - - - - - - - - - - - - -
more _____.

Home Activity Your child completed sentences using vocabulary words learned this week. Work together
on writing a story using these words. Ask your child the meanings of the words before your start working on
the story.

© Pearson Education 2

Look at the e-mail. **Write** the answer to each question.

⊠⊖⊕

| Write | Reply | Send | Forward | Delete | Address Book | Print |

FROM: Tyler Becker
TO: Jim Alcott
SUBJECT: Moving

Hi Jim,
I have some good news and some bad news. The good news is that my dad got a new job! The bad news is that we're moving. I will miss you. I'll tell you the rest when I see you at school.

Your friend,
Tyler

1. Who is this e-mail from?

_____

_____

2. What is the subject of the e-mail? _____

3. Which button do you click to answer? _____

4. Which button do you click to erase? _____

5. How is an e-mail different from a letter?

_____

_____

_____

Home Activity Your child learned how to use e-mail. Discuss ways you or your child could use e-mail. Write a pretend e-mail message together. Discuss the advantages and disadvantages of e-mail compared to regular postal mail.

© Pearson Education 2

Family Times

You are your child's first and best teacher!

This week we're

Reading Helen Keller and the Big Storm

Talking About How weather changes affect us

Learning About Vowels *oo, ue, ew, ui*
Fact and Opinion

© Pearson Education 2

Here are ways to help your child practice skills while having fun!

Day 1

Have your child read these words: *blue, cool, fruit, new.* For each word, have your child say a rhyming word with the same vowel spelling.

Day 2

Your child has been learning about statements of fact and opinion. Pick a topic, such as summer. Take turns making statements of fact and statements of opinion about summer.

Day 3

Have your child read these words: *angry, branches, clung, fingers, picnic, pressing, special.* Take turns giving clues and guessing the words.

Day 4

Have your child write these spelling words on slips of paper: *blue, clue, cool, drew, flew, fruit, juice, new, spoon, suit, too, true.* Take turns drawing words and using them in rhymes.

Day 5

This week your child has been reading and writing facts and opinions about storms. Have your child write a description of a storm. Ask your child to identify each sentence as a fact or opinion.

Fact Finder

Materials index cards, pencil, bag

Game Directions

1. Make a set of statement cards as shown. Put the cards in a bag.

2. Players take turns drawing a card, reading it aloud, and telling whether it contains a statement of fact or opinion.

3. Play continues until all statement cards have been used.

Thunder is scary.

Summer is the best season.

Rainy days are boring.

Low clouds cause fog.

Sleet is frozen rain.

Clouds hold water.

Spring rains are pretty.

Snow makes winter fun.

Storms can harm crops.

A tornado has strong winds.

© Pearson Education 2

Name _____

moon

gl**ue**

fr**ui**t

scr**ew**

Circle the word that has the same vowel sound as m**oo**n.
Write the word on the line.

1. blush   blue   blur

_____
_____

2. grew   grow   grain

_____
_____

3. stood   spun   spoon

_____
_____

4. just   joy   juice

_____
_____

5. flew   flow   fun

_____
_____

6. suit   south   shook

_____
_____

7. train   true   toad

_____
_____

8. club   clay   cool

_____
_____

© Pearson Education 2

Home Activity Your child wrote words that have the vowel sound in *moon*, spelled *oo* as in *moon*, *ue* as in *glue*, *ui* as in *fruit*, and *ew* as in *screw*. Write sentences using words with the vowel sound in *moon*, such as *food*, *bruise*, and *drew*. Have your child circle the words with this lesson's vowel sound.

Name _____

Read each sentence.
Underline the facts.
Circle the opinions.

1. Wind can blow dust.

2. It is no fun to play in the wind.

3. Wind cannot be seen with our eyes.

4. Wind can be hot or cold.

5. Everybody loves to fly kites in the wind.

_____

Write an **F** or an **O** to tell which sentence is
a **fact** or **opinion**.

6. Wind makes waves in the sea. _____

7. Sailing is more fun than windsurfing. _____

8. Wind blows the sand on the beach. _____

_____

Write one **fact** and one **opinion** about wind.

9. _____

10. _____

© Pearson Education 2

Home Activity Your child identified and wrote facts and opinions. Ask your child to describe his or her
favorite kind of weather. Then ask your child to give some facts and opinions about the weather.

Name _____

Read the story.
Follow the directions below.

The sport of windsurfing is exciting. There is a sail attached to a board. The wind catches the sail and moves the board across the water. Going fast is great fun.

Write two sentences from the story that are **facts**.

1. _____

2. _____

Write two sentences from the story that are **opinions**.

3. _____

4. _____

Write your own **opinion** about windsurfing.

5. _____

Home Activity Your child distinguished between facts and opinions. Together, read portions of a sports magazine or the sports section from the newspaper. As you read, ask your child to point out statements that are facts and opinions.

© Pearson Education 2

Name _____

Pick a word from the box to finish each sentence.
Write the word on the line.

> angry   branches   clung   fingers
> picnic   pressing   special

1. Our family was having a _____ lunch.

2. Suddenly, the tree _____ started moving.

3. The wind blew hard. My _____ got cold.

4. The sky got dark and thunder crashed.

   The sky seemed _____ .

5. Mom and I _____ to the blanket so it wouldn't blow away.

6. We were lucky that Dad had brought _____ coats that would keep us dry.

7. We ran to the car. The wind was _____ at my back. A big storm was on its way!

Home Activity Your child completed sentences using vocabulary words learned this week. Discuss with your child a time that your family encountered bad weather. Encourage your child to write a description of that experience using these vocabulary words.

46 Lesson Vocabulary

Practice Book Unit 4

© Pearson Education 2

Name _____

Read the story.
Follow the directions.

Dad and I went sailing last Friday. Dad said it's always good to be prepared when you sail. So we packed a lot of food and water. Dad made sure the weather radio was working. I also brought along our rain gear. Sure enough, it began to rain. Dad was right about being prepared.

Write the sentence that tells the **main idea**.

1. _____

Write three sentences that give more information about the main idea.

2. _____

3. _____

4. _____

5. Tell why you think the author wrote this story.

_____

Home Activity Your child identified the most important idea of a story and details that tell about the main idea. Select a favorite storybook and read the book together. Ask your child to identify the main idea of the story and some details that tell about the main idea.

© Pearson Education 2

Name _____

Pick a word from the box to match each clue.
Write the word on the line.

 b**oi**l   b**oy**

┌───┐
│   coin   enjoy   moist   point   spoil   voice   │
└───┘

1. You'll find it at the tip of a needle. _____

2. You use it to speak. _____

3. It means "a little wet." _____

4. You can use it to buy something. _____

5. It means "to be happy" with something. _____

6. It means "to become bad." _____

Circle the word for each picture.

7.
sail soil

8.
nurse noise

9.
roll royal

10.
cobweb cowboy

 Home Activity Your child reviewed words that have the vowel sound in *joy*, spelled *oi* as in *boil* and *oy* as in *boy*. Work with your child to write a story using as many *oi* and *oy* words as possible. Have your child highlight or circle each of the story words with the vowel sound in *joy*.

© Pearson Education 2

Name _____

Pick a word from the box to match each clue.
Write the word on the line.

angry   branches   clung   fingers
picnic   pressing   special

"arms" of a tree

1. _____

one of a kind

2. _____

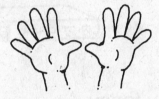

3. _____

4. _____

pushing with your fingers

5. _____

held tightly

6. _____

mad

7. _____

© Pearson Education 2

Home Activity Your child completed sentences using vocabulary words learned this week. Select family photos to discuss a family picnic and what the weather was like. Encourage your child to describe the experience, using these vocabulary words.

Name _____

Circle the picture or pictures that best answer each question.

1. **Circle one** you would use to see the state where Helen Keller was born.

 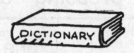 

2. **Circle one** that would tell the story of Helen Keller's life.

3. **Circle one** that would tell if a storm is likely today.

4. **Circle two** you could use to find facts about storms.

5. **Circle one** that could tell you what it's like to be blind.

 Home Activity Your child learned about choosing reference sources. Discuss resources you use when you need information. Ask your child what two resources he or she could use to find out about life long ago. Remind your child that a grandparent or older friend might also be a resource.

50 **Research and Study Skills** Choose Reference Sources **Practice Book Unit 4**

© Pearson Education 2

© Pearson Education 2

Family Times

You are your child's first and best teacher!

This week we're

Reading Firefighter!

Talking About Why it's important to do a good job

Learning About Suffixes -ly, -ful, -er, -or

Main Idea and Supporting Details

Here are ways to help your child practice skills while having fun!

Day 1

Have your child read these words: *visitor, helper, cheerful, weekly*. Ask what base word (*visit*) and suffix (*-or*) make up each word.

Day 2

Your child has practiced identifying the main idea and supporting details in text. Read a story without showing the title. Ask your child to make up a title that says what the story is all about.

Day 3

Have your child read these words: *building, burning, masks, quickly, roar, station, tightly*. Ask your child to use these words in sentences that tell what he or she knows about firefighters.

Day 4

Have your child write the following spelling words: *cheerful, fighter, graceful, hardly, helper, quickly, sailor, slowly, teacher, visitor, weekly, yearly*. Have your child draw a symbol to represent each word, such as a happy face for *cheerful* or ocean waves for *sailor*.

Day 5

This week your child has identified details and discussed what it means to do a good job. Have your child write a paragraph with details that tell about a good job he or she has done.

Lift and Spell

Materials white paper, scissors, pencil, paper clip, buttons

Game Directions

1. Make a simple spinner as shown. Place a button above each word on the game board.
2. Players take turns spinning a suffix, picking a word, adding the suffix, and spelling the new word. If correct, the player takes the button.
3. Play continues until all the buttons are taken.

-ly	-er
-ful	-or

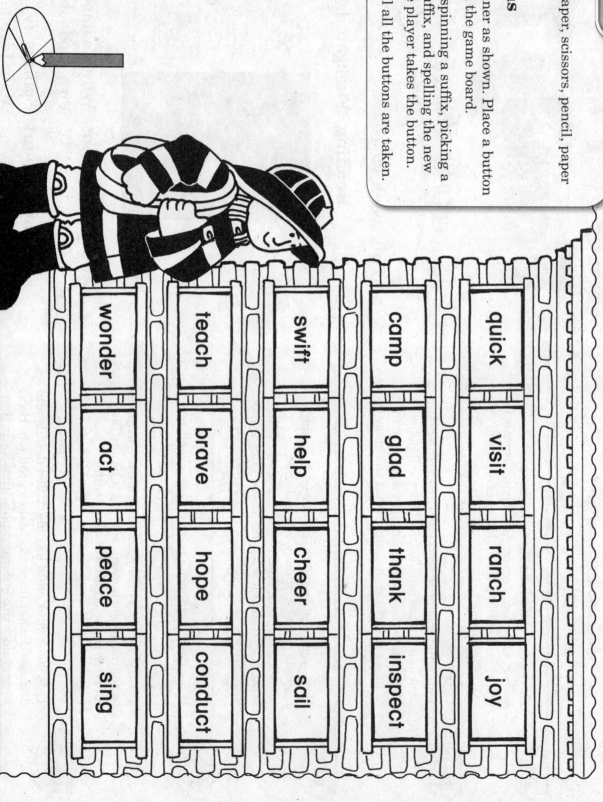

wonder	act	peace	sing
teach	brave	hope	conduct
swift	help	cheer	sail
camp	glad	thank	inspect
quick	visit	ranch	joy

© Pearson Education 2

teach + er = teach**er**   sail + or = sail**or**

Add er or **or** to each word to make a word from the box.
Write the new word on the line.

| actor   camper   fighter   helper   singer   visitor |

visit
_____
- - - - - - - - - - - - - - - - - -
1._____

camp
_____
- - - - - - - - - - - - - - - - - -
2._____

sing
_____
- - - - - - - - - - - - - - - - - -
3._____

act
_____
- - - - - - - - - - - - - - - - - -
4._____

fight
_____
- - - - - - - - - - - - - - - - - -
5._____

help
_____
- - - - - - - - - - - - - - - - - -
6._____

slow + ly = slow**ly**   cheer + ful = cheer**ful**

Add ly or **ful** to each word to make a new word.
Write the new word on the line.

Add -ly   **Add -ful**

week
_____
- - - - - - - - - - - - - - - - - -
7._____

joy
_____
- - - - - - - - - - - - - - - - - -
8._____

quick
_____
- - - - - - - - - - - - - - - - - -
9._____

hope
_____
- - - - - - - - - - - - - - - - - -
10._____

Home Activity Your child wrote words with the suffixes *-ly, -ful, -er,* and *-or.* Help your child write sentences, using the words from this page. Ask your child to read each sentence and circle the *-ly, -ful, -er,* or *-or* suffix in each lesson word.

© Pearson Education 2

Name _____

Read the paragraph. **Follow** the directions.

Fire moves quickly. That is why each family member needs to know what to do in a fire. If a smoke alarm rings, get out. Make sure someone helps any young children or older people. Once you get out, stay out. Call for help after you get outside.

1. **Circle** the answer below that tells what the paragraph is about.
   using smoke alarms   what to do in a fire   calling for help

2. **Circle** the answer below that tells the most important idea about the paragraph.
   Each family member needs to know what to do in a fire.
   Once you get out, stay out.
   Call for help after you get outside.

3. **Underline** the sentence in the paragraph that tells what to do if a smoke alarm rings.

4. **Circle** the sentence in the paragraph that tells when to call for help.

5. **Write** a title for this paragraph.

_____

_____

_____

© Pearson Education 2

Home Activity Your child identified the main idea in a paragraph about fire safety. With your child, read a magazine article or book about community helpers, such as police or firefighters. Stop to talk about the most important idea in each paragraph.

Name _____

Look at the picture. **Read** the paragraph. **Follow** the directions.

Forest fires burn quickly when it is windy and dry. Firefighters try to keep the fire from growing. Sometimes planes drop water on the fire. Firefighters also chop down trees and grass around the fire. This takes away the dry plants that feed the fire.

1. What do you think the picture is mostly about? Circle your answer below.

   forest fires   planes   trees

2. **Pick** the best title for the paragraph. **Circle** your answer below.
   How to Cut Down Trees
   Water Puts Out Fires
   Fighting Forest Fires

3. **Draw** a picture to show a detail of what the paragraph is about.

4. **Write** a sentence that tells about the detail in your picture.

   _____

   _____

   _____

Home Activity Your child identified the main idea and important details in a paragraph about forest fires. Read a story or nonfiction selection to your child. Ask your child to draw a picture that shows the main idea of the text.

© Pearson Education 2

Name _____

Pick a word from the box to match each clue.
Write the word on the line.

building burning masks quickly
roar station tightly

1.

_____

_____

2.

_____

_____

3. firmly

_____

_____

4. on fire

_____

_____

5. not slowly

_____

_____

6. where firefighters work

_____

_____

7. a loud, deep sound

_____

_____

Home Activity Your child used clues to identify and write words that he or she learned to read this week.
Work with your child to write a story about firefighters, using as many of the listed words as possible.

Practice Book Unit 5

© Pearson Education 2

Read the paragraph. **Follow** the directions.

Fire Safety
by Liz Stone

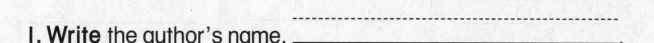

One way to fight fires is with fire safety. Firefighters sometimes visit schools to talk to children. They show what to do if there is a fire. They teach how to keep fires from starting. They also remind people to use smoke alarms.

1. **Write** the author's name. _____.

2. **Circle** the word below that tells what the paragraph is all about.
   safety   smoke   school

3. **Underline** the name of something in the paragraph that firefighters want people to use.

4. **Circle** a word in the paragraph that tells where firefighters might talk to children.

5. **Write** a sentence that tells why you think the author wrote this paragraph.

_____

_____

_____

Home Activity Your child answered questions about nonfiction text and explained why the author wrote it. Write a list of fire safety rules for your home and family. Help your child read the rules. Ask your child to explain why you wrote these rules.

© Pearson Education 2

Name _____

 moon   glue    fruit   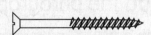 screw

Circle the word for each picture.
Write the word on the line.

1. nose   news

_____

2. noon   now

_____

3. stood   stew

_____

4. club   clue

_____

5. juice   just

_____

6. brown   broom

_____

Find the word that has the same vowel sound as the picture.
Mark the space to show your answer.

7. ◯ flew   ◯ feet   ◯ foot

8. ◯ tray   ◯ too   ◯ tie

 Home Activity Your child reviewed words that have the vowel sound *oo* as in *moon*, *ue* as in *glue*, *ui* as in *fruit*, and *ew* as in *screw*. Write the following words on small slips of paper: *tool, pool, clue, true, chew, dew, boot, suit*. Mix them up. Have your child read the words and then match the words that rhyme.

© Pearson Education 2

Name _____

Pick a word from the box to finish the sentence.
Write the word on the line.

> building   burning   masks
> quickly   roar   station   tightly

1. A call comes to the fire _____ .

2. A _____ is on fire!

3. The firefighters move _____ .

4. They grab their boots and _____ .

5. The truck races to the _____ home.

6. You can hear the siren _____ .

7. They hold on _____ to the hoses.

Home Activity Your child used lesson vocabulary words to complete sentences. Ask your child to use the vocabulary words to make up sentences about the jobs that firefighters do. Work together to write the sentences, and encourage your child to illustrate them.

© Pearson Education 2

Name _____

Read the Glossary and **answer** the questions.

Glossary

able · button

Aa able   (AY bul) If you have the power or skill to do
something, you are **able**.
Tom was **able** to lift the heavy box. ADJECTIVE

add   (ad) If you join one thing to another, you **add**.
Mom will **add** some apples to the bowl of oranges.
VERB

Bb buried (BAIR eed) Something that is **buried** is hidden or
covered up.
The dog **buried** the bone. VERB

button (BUT un) You use a round, flat object called a **button**
on clothes to hold parts together.
Jodi lost a **button** on her skirt. NOUN

I. Which word is an adjective? _____

2. Which word could describe a hidden treasure?

_____

_____   _____

3. Which word is a noun? _____

4. **Circle** the one that has the same vowel sound in *able*.
   a as in **hat**   a as in **age**   a as in **far**

5. **Circle** the one that matches the vowel sound in *button*.
   u as in **cup**   u as in **put**   u as in **huge**

Home Activity Your child learned how to use a Glossary. Ask your child to read each word and its
definition. Then have your child make up a sentence, using each word.

© Pearson Education 2

Name _____

Family Times

You are your child's first and best teacher!

This week we're

Reading One Dark Night

Talking About Why we should take care of animals

Learning About Prefixes *un-, re-, pre-, dis-*
Sequence

© Pearson Education 2

Here are ways to help your child practice skills while having fun!

Day 1

Have your child read the words *disagree, pregame, rewind,* and *unpack* and identify each prefix and base word.

Day 2

Your child has identified the sequence of events in text. Read a story and ask your child to retell the story in order.

Day 3

Have your child read these words: *flashes, lightning, pounds, pours, rolling, storm, thunder.* Take turns using these words to describe storms.

Day 4

Have your child write the following spelling words on slips of paper: *disagree, disappear, preheat, preschool, regroup, rerun, retie, rewind, unlock, unpack, unplug, unsafe.* Mix the words. Sort the words according to prefixes.

Day 5

This week your child used a graphic organizer (a series of boxes) to show sequence. Have your child complete a graphic organizer to show what he or she does each morning to get ready for school.

Ready, Set, Go!

Materials index cards, crayons or markers

Game Directions

1. Make a set of picture cards as shown.
2. Players each get cards for one story. Players mix the story cards and place them face down.
3. On a signal, players turn over their cards and put them in order. The first player to get the story cards in correct order goes first to retell the story.

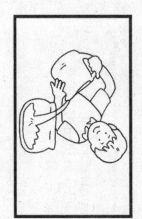

© Pearson Education 2

Name _____

un + happy = **un**happy

pre + game = **pre**game

re + paint = **re**paint

dis + appear = **dis**appear

> disagree   disloyal   prepay   preteen   replay
> reread   retie   unsafe   unlocked   unpack

Write words with **un-**, **re-**, **pre-**, or **dis-** to match each clue.
Use the words in the box if you need help.

I. play again

_____

- - - - - - - - - - - - - - - - -

_____

2. not agree

_____

- - - - - - - - - - - - - - - - -

_____

3. opposite of pack

_____

- - - - - - - - - - - - - - - - -

_____

4. pay in advance

_____

- - - - - - - - - - - - - - - - -

_____

5. not locked

_____

- - - - - - - - - - - - - - - - -

_____

6. not loyal

_____

- - - - - - - - - - - - - - - - -

_____

7. not yet a teen

_____

- - - - - - - - - - - - - - - - -

_____

8. tie again

_____

- - - - - - - - - - - - - - - - -

_____

9. not safe

_____

- - - - - - - - - - - - - - - - -

_____

10. read again

_____

- - - - - - - - - - - - - - - - -

_____

Home Activity Your child wrote words with the prefixes *un-*, *re-*, *pre-*, and *dis-*. With your child, look for words like these in ads and signs. Help your child pronounce the words and figure out what they mean. Encourage your child to use the meaning of the prefix to help define the word.

© Pearson Education 2

Name _____

Look at the pictures.
Write the words **first, second, third,** and **last** to show the correct order of events.

_____
- -

_____
- -

_____
- -

_____
- -

Write a sentence about what might happen next.

_____
- -
_____
- -
_____

© Pearson Education 2

 School + Home **Home Activity** Your child identified the order of events in a picture story about a boy and his dog. Have your child draw four or five pictures that tell a different story about a child and pet. Ask your child to label the pictures to show the order of events.

Name _____

Read the story. **Follow** the directions.

Winter was coming. The birds needed food. Carla wanted to help. First, she asked her mother. Then she made a bird feeder. After that, Carla filled it with seed. Finally, Carla put the feeder in the tree.

1. **Underline** the clue words **First, Then, After,** and **Finally** in the story.

2. **Show** the right order. Write **1, 2, 3,** or **4** on the lines.

_____ Finally, Carla put the bird feeder in the tree.

_____ First, she asked her mother.

_____ After that, Carla filled it with seed.

_____ Then she made a bird feeder.

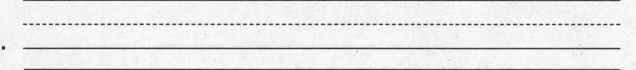

Write a sentence to tell what might happen next.

3. _____

_____

_____

_____

© Pearson Education 2

School + Home **Home Activity** Your child identified words that show the order of events and placed story events in correct order. Talk with your child about something he or she could do to help with the care of a pet or with another household task. Together, write the steps your child would follow to accomplish the job.

Name _____

Pick a word from the box to match each clue.
Write the word on the line.

> flashes   lightning   pounds
> pours   rolling
> storm   thunder

1. a sound that comes with lightning

_____
- - - - - - - - - - - - - - - - -
_____

2. light that comes before thunder

_____
- - - - - - - - - - - - - - - - -
_____

3. short bursts of light

_____
- - - - - - - - - - - - - - - - -
_____

4. beats down

_____
- - - - - - - - - - - - - - - - -
_____

5. making rumbling sounds

_____
- - - - - - - - - - - - - - - - -
_____

6. It brings rain and wind.

_____
- - - - - - - - - - - - - - - - -
_____

7. When it rains hard, it

_____
- - - - - - - - - - - - - - - - -
_____ .

Home Activity Your child used clues to identify and write words that he or she learned to read this week. Ask your child to think of a storm he or she has experienced. Use the words from this page to help your child write a paragraph describing the storm.

© Pearson Education 2

Name _____

Read the story. **Follow** the directions.

Rob wanted a pet more than anything. He begged for a dog. His mom said, "No." Dogs need a yard. Rob begged for a cat. His mom said, "No." Cats make her nose itch. He asked for a fish. This time she said, "Yes." Later that day Rob picked out a big, beautiful fish. It was just the right pet for him.

Circle the sentence below that tells the big idea of this story.

Dogs need space to run.

Cats make some people sick.

A pet must be right for your family.

Write 1, 2, or **3** on the lines to show the right order.

_____ Rob's mom said, "No."

_____ Rob got a fish.

_____ Rob begged for a dog.

Home Activity Your child identified the big idea of a story and put story events in correct order. Pick a simple story that your child knows well. Talk about the story's big idea. Tell the story, but change the order of key events. Then ask your child to retell the story, putting the events into the right order.

© Pearson Education 2

Name _____

Pick a word from the box to match each clue.
Write the letters of the word in each puzzle.

harmful   inventor   painter   softly   useful   yearly

1. not loudly

2. artist

3. every summer

4. bad for you

5. of help

6. a person who makes
   up something new

1. ▢ ▢ ◯ ▢ ▢ ▢

2. ▢ ◯ ▢ ▢ ▢ ▢ ▢

3. ▢ ▢ ▢ ◯ ▢ ▢

4. ▢ ▢ ▢ ◯ ▢ ▢

5. ▢ ▢ ◯ ▢ ▢ ▢

6. ▢ ▢ ▢ ▢ ▢ ▢ ◯

Put these letters in order to write a word.
HINT: The circled letters in the words
above spell the new word.

_____

rerfam -

© Pearson Education 2

School + Home

Home Activity Your child reviewed words with the suffixes *-ly, -ful, -er,* and *-or.* Help your child write a story using some of this lesson's words. Encourage your child to include other words with suffixes. Have your child circle each *-ly, -ful, -er,* and *-or* suffix and read the story aloud.

Name _____

Pick a word from the box to finish each sentence.
Write the word on the line.

flashes   lightning   pounds   pours
rolling   storm   thunder

1. The kitten cries as the rain _____ the car.

2. Rain _____ off the roof.

3. The _____ thunder continues.

4. The sky fills with flashes of _____ .

5. The kitten closes its eyes from the _____ .

6. Just then comes a loud clap of _____ .

7. Why are you out in this _____ , little kitty?

© Pearson Education 2

Home Activity Your child used lesson vocabulary words to complete sentences. Write different sentences and have a blank line for your child to fill in the correct vocabulary word for each sentence.

Name _____

Look at the bar graph. **Write** the answer to each question.

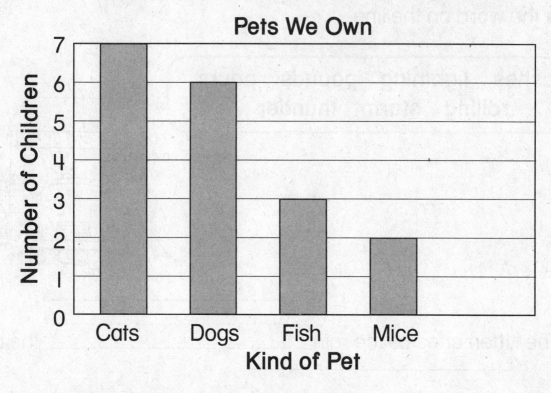

Pets We Own

Number of Children

7
6
5
4
3
2
1
0

Cats   Dogs   Fish   Mice

Kind of Pet

1. What does the bar graph show?

_____
- -
_____
- -
_____

2. How many children own dogs? _____   _____

3. How many more children own cats than fish? _____

4. Which animal is most popular? _____

5. A new girl in class has a bird. Add that pet to the chart.

Home Activity Your child learned how to read a bar graph. Have your child ask friends and relatives which pet they like best. Keep a tally of how people respond. Help your child make a bar graph showing what kind of pets people prefer.

© Pearson Education 2

© Pearson Education 2

Family Times

Name

You are your child's first and best teacher!

This week we're

Reading Bad Dog, Dodger!

Talking About: How we can be responsible family members

Learning About Silent Consonants
Plot and Theme

Here are ways to help your child practice skills while having fun!

Day 1
Have your child read these words: *knock, sign, thumb, wrap.* Have your child name the silent letter in each word (*k, g, b, w*).

Day 2
Your child has been learning about plot and theme. After reading a story, ask your child what problem the main character had to overcome. Ask how the character worked it out.

Day 3
Have your child read these words: *chased, chewing, dripping, grabbed, practice, treat, wagged.* Work together to use the words in a story about a new puppy.

Day 4
Have your child write the following spelling words: *climb, comb, gnat, knee, knob, knock, lamb, sign, wrap, wren, write, wrong.* Have your child underline in each word the two letters that stand for one sound.

Day 5
This week your child learned when to use *I* and *me.* Have your child use *I* and *me* to write a poem. Help your child choose a title for the poem.

Silence Is Golden

Materials paper, pencil, paper bag, button

Game Directions

1. Write the words below on slips of paper and put them in a bag.

2. Players take turns picking a word from the bag and reading it aloud. Players must toss a button on the game board and land on the picture for that word to earn a point. If a player misses, the word is put back in the bag.

3. Play continues until each word has been used.

Words with Silent Consonants

climb, comb, gnat, knob, knot, lamb, sign, wrist, write

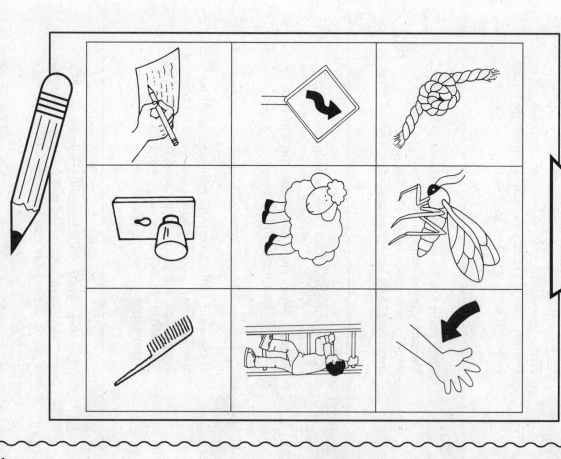

© Pearson Education 2

Name _____

<u>kn</u>ee   la<u>mb</u>   <u>wr</u>ist   si<u>gn</u>

Say the word for each picture.
Write kn, wr, gn, or **mb** to finish each word.

1. _____ ench

2. co _____

3. _____ ob

4. _____ at

5. cli _____

6. _____ ite

7. _____ ock

8. thu _____

Find the word that has the same beginning sound as the picture.
Mark the space to show your answer.

9.
◯ wrong
◯ wing
◯ white

10.
◯ king
◯ knife
◯ kick

Home Activity Your child completed words where two letters together stand for only one sound, as in *knee, wrist, sign,* and *lamb.* Work with your child to write sentences using the *kn, wr, gn,* and *mb* words on this page. Have your child read and illustrate each sentence.

© Pearson Education 2

Name _____

Read the story.
Follow the directions.

Bill had a new puppy. Carmen was going to see it. Then her mom got sick, and Carmen had to take care of her little brother. Carmen knew she needed to help out. She asked Bill to bring the puppy to her house. Carmen's mom took a nap. Everybody else had fun in the yard.

1. **Underline** the sentence that tells about Carmen's problem.

2. **Draw two lines** under the sentence that tells what Carmen did about her problem.

3. **Circle** the sentence below that tells how Bill helped Carmen.
   Bill got a new puppy.
   Bill asked Carmen to come to his house.
   Bill took the puppy to Carmen's house.

4. **Circle** the sentence below that tells the big idea of this story.
   Sometimes people get sick.
   Everyone likes puppies.
   Family members help each other.

5. **Circle** the parts of the story that helped you tell the big idea.

Home Activity Your child identified the problem, solution, and big idea in a story. Work with your child to come up with an idea you both think is important, such as: *It's important to try.* Help your child write about something that has happened in his or her life that conveys that idea.

© Pearson Education 2

Name _____

Read the story. **Follow** the directions.

Maria had a new puppy named Sunny. Sunny chewed Maria's doll. He ate her homework. Maria worked with Sunny. Sunny got better, but he still got into things. Then Maria trained herself. She picked up her toys and papers. Now Sunny no longer eats Maria's things.

1. **Circle** the sentence below that tells the big idea of this story.
   Puppies like to chew things.
   People and puppies may both need training.
   Puppies are a lot of work.

2. **Underline two sentences** in the story that show how Maria finally got the puppy to stop eating her things.

Write 1, 2, or 3 on the lines to show the right order.

_____

_____ 3. Sunny chewed Maria's doll.

_____ 4. Maria had a new puppy named Sunny.

_____ 5. Now Sunny no longer eats Maria's things.

Write a sentence that tells something that happened in the middle of the story.

_____

6. _____

Home Activity Your child identified the big idea of a story and put story events in correct order. Read a story aloud to your child. Have your child tell what happened in the *beginning, middle,* and *end* of the story. Ask your child what he or she learned from the story.

© Pearson Education 2

Name _____

Pick a word from the box to match each clue.
Write the letters of the word in each puzzle.
The circled letters spell two words.

| chased | chewing | dripping | grabbed |
| practice | treat | wagged | |

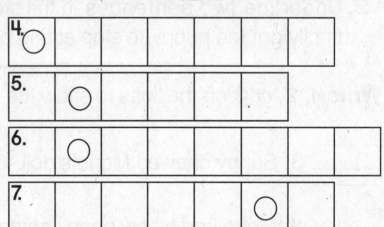

1. to do over and over

2. ran after

3. something good to eat

4. crushing with the teeth

5. moved the tail

6. drops falling

7. took

What do people do for animals? HINT: Find the words hidden in the circles above.

_____   _____
- - - - - - - - - - - - - - - -   - - - - - - - - - - - - - - - -
_____   _____

© Pearson Education 2

 School + Home **Home Activity** Your child used clues to identify new vocabulary words. Play a game of charades with your child. Take turns acting out clues and guessing the vocabulary words on this page. Invite other family members or friends to play the game with you.

Name _____

Look at the pictures.
Write the words **first, second, third,** and **last** to show the correct order of events.

_____
- - - - - - - - - - - - - - - -
_____ I.

_____
- - - - - - - - - - - - - - - -
_____ 2.

_____
- - - - - - - - - - - - - - - -
_____ 3.

_____
- - - - - - - - - - - - - - - -
_____ 4.

LEAF BAGS

5. Write a sentence about what might happen next.

_____
- -
_____
_____
- -
_____

© Pearson Education 2

 School + Home **Home Activity** Your child identified the order of events in a picture story about a boy and his mother working together. Work with your child to write a story about a project you and your child did together. Encourage your child to use words such as *first, next,* and *last* to show the sequence of events.

Name _____

un + happy =   pre + game =   re + paint =   dis + appear =
unhappy   **pre**game   **re**paint   **dis**appear

---

dislike   distrust   prepay   pretest
remake   rewrite   unlock   unripe

Pick a word from the box that is the opposite of each word below.
Write the word on the line.

I. like

_____

2. ripe

_____

3. trust

_____

4. lock

_____

Pick a word from the box that means the same as each group of
words. **Write** the word on the line.

5. make again

_____

6. a test before a big test

_____

7. write again

_____

8. pay ahead of time

_____

© Pearson Education 2

Home Activity Your child reviewed words with the prefixes *un-*, *re-*, *pre-*, and *dis-*. Work with your child to write a list of words with these prefixes. Have your child read each word and draw a picture to show its meaning.

Name _____

Pick a word from the box to finish the sentence.
Write the word on the line.

> chased   chewing   dripping   grabbed
> practice   treat   wagged

1. Our new puppy always _____ the cat.

2. He also likes _____ Mom's slippers.

3. One time he got _____ wet in the rain.

4. The puppy _____ my rain hat and ran.

5. Then he looked at me and _____ his tail.

6. So I trained him and made him _____ .

7. I gave him a _____ for being good.

School + Home

Home Activity Your child used lesson vocabulary to complete sentences. Work with your child to use these vocabulary words in a poem or song about a playful puppy and to perform it for other family members or friends.

© Pearson Education 2

Name _____

Look at the picture. **Answer** each question.

1. Which volume would you use to find out about dogs?

_____

- -

_____

2. What key word might you use to find facts about pets?

_____

- -

_____

3. What key word might you use to find facts about baseball?

_____

- -

_____

4. Between which pair of guide words might you find an entry
   for **animal**? **Circle** the correct answer.
   acorn / Adler   air / alligator   amber / ape

5. Between which pair of guide words might you find an entry
   for **school**? **Circle** the correct answer.
   Saturn / seal   sky / slug   snow / space

© Pearson Education 2

School + Home

Home Activity Your child learned how to use an encyclopedia. Ask your child to name a topic for possible
research and explain how an encyclopedia can be used to find related information. If possible, go to the
library and have your child use the encyclopedia.

© Pearson Education 2

Name

Family Times

You are your child's first and best teacher!

This week we're

Reading Horace and Morris but
mostly Dolores

Talking About What good friends and
neighbors do

Learning About *ph, gh* /f/
Author's Purpose

---

*Here are ways to help your child practice
skills while having fun!*

Day 1

Have your child read these words: *laugh,
phone, graph, rough.* Ask what sound the
underlined letters stand for in each word.

Day 2

Your child has been discussing why authors
write, such as to share, explain, or tell. After
reading a story or short article with your child,
ask why the author wrote it.

Day 3

Have your child read these words: *adventure,
climbed, clubhouse, exploring, greatest, truest,
wondered.* Use the words to act out a scene in
a pretend children's clubhouse.

Day 4

Have your child write the following spelling
words: *cliff, cough, enough, giraffe, graph,
laugh, phone, photo, puff, rough, stuff, tough.*
Have your child underline the letter or letters
in each word that stand for the /f/ sound.

Day 5

This week your child learned about puns, word
play that involves a word with two meanings
or two words that sound nearly the same.
Help your child make up some puns and write
them. Example: Mount Ever-Rust.

Paint It!

Materials yellow and orange crayons

Game Directions

1. Players take turns reading the words on the fence.

2. If a word has the /f/ sound, spelled *ph* or *gh*, color the board yellow. If the word does not have the /f/ sound, color the board orange.

cough
trophy
poppy
phone
tough
signal
orphan
explain
laughter
phrase

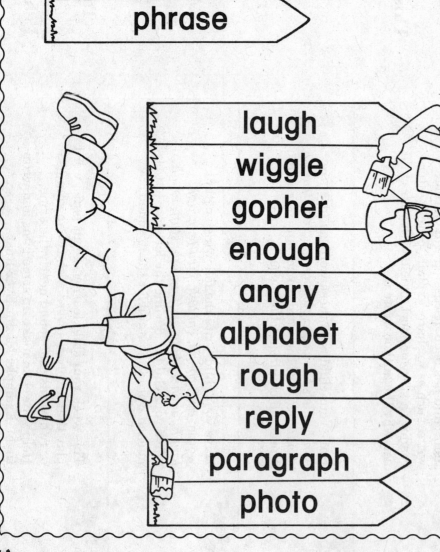

laugh
wiggle
gopher
enough
angry
alphabet
rough
reply
paragraph
photo

© Pearson Education 2

cough dolphin elephant graph laugh
photo phrase rough trophy

phone   lau**gh**

Pick a word from the box to match each clue.
Write the word on the line.

1.

2.

3.

_____
- - - - - - - - - - -
_____

4. not smooth   **5.** a water animal   **6.** a few words

_____
- - - - - - - - - - -
_____

Unscramble the letters to make a word from the box.
Write the word on the line.

7. topoh   **8.** aulgh   **9.** phrag

_____
- - - - - - - - - - -
_____

 Home Activity Your child wrote words with the consonant sound /f/, spelled *ph* as in *phone* and *gh* as in *laugh*. Help your child write a poem or song using the lesson words. Encourage your child to read or perform the work for friends or family.

Practice Book Unit 5   **Phonics** *ph, gh/f/* **83**

© Pearson Education 2

Name _____

Read the passage. **Follow** the directions.

A New Park
by Al Turner

Last weekend our neighbors worked together. We turned an empty lot into a park. Everybody helped. I pulled weeds. Nate picked up litter. Mom helped to build the slide. Now we have a great place to play.

1. **Circle** the name of the author.

2. **Circle** the answer below that tells what the story is all about.

   Al   a new park   a new slide

3. **Circle** the words in the story that tell when they made the park.

4. **Underline** three ways that tell how people worked on the park.

5. **Write** a sentence that tells why you think the author wrote this story.

© Pearson Education 2

Home Activity Your child read and answered questions about a story and told why the author wrote it. Work with your child to write a paragraph about something of interest in your child's life. Have your child read and explain the purpose of the paragraph.

Name _____

Read the story.
Follow the directions.

Work Party
by Kate Mason

Does your school or park need work? Hold a work party. First, pick a date. Then, make some signs. Next, get the supplies you need. Don't forget to bring food and drinks on work day. Finally, say thanks to those who helped.

1. **Circle** the name of the author.

2. **Circle** the words below that tell what the story is all about.
   signs   a work party   parks and schools

3. **Underline** three things to do before the work day.

4. **Circle** the words that tell what to do last.

5. **Write** why you think the author wrote this passage.

_____

- -

_____

_____

- -

© Pearson Education 2

School + Home **Home Activity** Your child read and answered questions about a story and told why the author wrote it. Work with your child to write a paragraph that shares something funny that happened in your neighborhood. Have your child read the paragraph and explain his or her purpose for writing.

Name _____

Pick a word from the box to match each clue.
Write the word on the line.

adventure   climbed   clubhouse   exploring
greatest   truest   wondered

1. where the club meets _____

2. the very best _____

3. an exciting trip or event _____

4. wanted to know _____

5. the most loyal _____

6. hiked up _____

7. looking around a new place _____

 Home Activity Your child used word clues to practice writing new vocabulary words. Make up a simple crossword puzzle with your child using some of these vocabulary words. Use the clues above or write some of your own.

© Pearson Education 2

Name _____

Read the story. **Follow** the directions.

Sandy looked outside. All she saw were weeds. Sandy had a plan. We must build a garden! Sandy talked to her neighbors. Soon everyone got to work. By summer they had a beautiful garden. Now people smile when they see what they made together.

1. **Circle** the sentence below that tells the big idea.
   Gardens are beautiful.
   People can work together to make things better.
   Gardens grow in the spring.

2. **Write** 1, 2, or 3 on the lines to show the right order.

_____ They had a beautiful garden.

_____ Sandy talked to her neighbors.

_____ Everyone got to work.

3. **Write** a sentence that tells something that happened in the beginning of the story.

_____

_____

_____

_____

Home Activity Your child identified the big idea of a story and put story events in correct order. Work with your child to write another story about friends or neighbors working together. As you plan your writing, discuss what happens in the *beginning*, *middle*, and *end* of the story.

© Pearson Education 2

Name _____

knee   wrist   sign   lamb

Circle a word to finish each sentence.
Write the word on the line.

right   wrote

_____

- -

1. The teacher _____ the problem.

sign   swan

_____

- -

2. She drew a plus _____ .

knew   now

_____

- -

3. She asked who _____ the answer.

them   thumb

_____

- -

4. I snapped my finger and _____.

no   know

_____

- -

5. "I _____ the right number," I said.

© Pearson Education 2

 School + Home   **Home Activity** Your child reviewed words where two letters together stand for one sound, as in *knee*, *wrist*, *sign*, and *lamb*. Write some other words with these sounds, such as *knot*, *knock*, *wrap*, *wrench*, *design*, *gnome*, *comb*, and *climb*. Ask your child to read and illustrate each word.

Name _____

Pick a word from the box to finish the sentence.
Write the word on the line.

> adventure   climbed   clubhouse   exploring
> greatest   truest   wondered

_____

1. Today we met at our _____ .

_____

2. Only our _____ friends came.

_____

3. We _____ what to do.

_____

4. Then Max had the _____ plan.

_____

5. We would go on an _____ !

_____

6. We had fun _____ .

_____

7. We _____ into bed and fell asleep.

Home Activity Your child used lesson vocabulary words to complete sentences. Ask your child to describe an adventure he or she would like to take and write an adventure story together. Try to use as many of the vocabulary words as possible.

© Pearson Education 2

Name _____

Read the table. **Write** the answer to each question.

Family Chores

Person	Job
Stan	Set the table
Nate	Take out the trash
Dean	Wash the dishes
Emmy	Dry the dishes
Mom	Cook Monday–Friday
Dad	Cook Saturday–Sunday

1. What does the table show?

_____
- -
_____

2. What is Nate's job?

_____
- -
_____

3. What is Emmy's job?

_____
- -
_____

_____
- - - - - - - - - - - - - - - - -
4. Who sets the table? _____

_____
- - - - - - - - - - - - - - - - -
5. Who cooks on the weekends? _____

Home Activity Your child learned how to read a table. Work with your child to make a table of chore assignments. Ask your child to explain the table to others in the household. As household responsibilities change, ask your child to make new tables and explain them.

© Pearson Education 2

Family Times

You are your child's first and best teacher!

This week we're

Reading The Signmaker's Assistant

Talking About What happens when we do the wrong thing

Learning About Vowels *aw, au, augh, al* Realism and Fantasy

© Pearson Education 2

Here are ways to help your child practice skills while having fun!

Day 1

Have your child read these words: *raw, sauce, daughter, walk.* Help your child list other words with the same vowel sound and spellings.

Day 2

Your child has been discussing realism and fantasy. As you read a story together, discuss which parts could happen and which could not happen.

Day 3

Have your child read the words *afternoon, blame, idea, important, signmaker,* and *townspeople* and make a comic strip using them. Help draw the pictures.

Day 4

Have your child write these spelling words: *August, auto, because, caught, chalk, draw, fault, launch, talk, taught, thaw, walk.* Rewrite each word to scramble the letters (as in *tauo* for *auto*). Have your child unscramble the letters and write each word correctly.

Day 5

This week your child practiced persuasive writing. Have your child write a letter that tries to convince you to serve a favorite meal.

Maybe, Maybe Not

Materials white paper, scissors, pencil, paper clip, buttons

Game Directions

1. Make a simple spinner as shown.

2. Players take turns moving a button to the next block on the game board and following the commands. If the block shows a picture, the player spins the spinner.

3. If the spinner points to **realism**, players tell something that could happen to solve the problem on the game board. If the spinner points to **fantasy**, players make up something that **could not** happen.

4. Play continues until all the players reach "End."

fantasy

realism

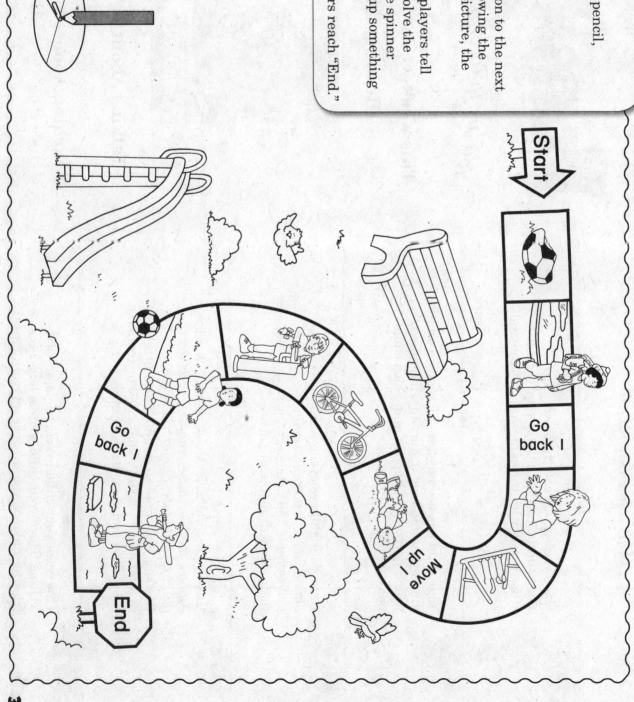

Start

Go back 1

Go back 1

Move up 1

Go back 1

End

© Pearson Education 2

Name _____

s<u>aw</u>   <u>au</u>to   c<u>augh</u>t   ch<u>al</u>k

Write a word from the box to match each picture.

daughter draw fall naughty raw sauce thaw walk

1. _____
_ _ _ _ _ _ _

2. _____
_ _ _ _ _ _ _

3. _____
_ _ _ _ _ _ _

4. _____
_ _ _ _ _ _ _

Write a word from the box that is the opposite of each word below.

freeze
_____
5. _ _ _ _ _ _ _

rise
_____
6. _ _ _ _ _ _ _

good
_____
7. _ _ _ _ _ _ _

cooked
_____
8. _ _ _ _ _ _ _

Mark the space for the word that has the vowel sound in **saw**.

9. ◯ fault
◯ find
◯ few

10. ◯ tray
◯ took
◯ taught

School + Home **Home Activity** Your child wrote words with the vowel sound in *fall*, spelled *aw* as in *saw*, *au* as in *auto*, *augh* as in *caught*, and *al* as in *chalk*. Hold a spelling bee with your child. Say a word. Have your child repeat the word and then spell it aloud or write it.

© Pearson Education 2

Name _____

Read each sentence.
Write yes if it tells something that could really happen.
Write no if it tells something that could not really happen.

_____ 1. Ben left the door open.

_____ 2. The cat ran out.

_____ 3. Ben got a plane to look for the cat.

_____ 4. The cat's friends looked too.

_____ 5. Finally, the cat called home.

School + Home **Home Activity** Your child determined whether events in a story could really happen. Think of a story your child knows well. Discuss whether the story could really happen or not. Encourage your child to tell what made the story a realistic story or a fantasy.

94 **Comprehension** Realism and Fantasy

Practice Book Unit 5

Name _____

Look at each picture.
Circle R if the picture shows something that could happen.
Circle F if the picture shows something that could not happen.

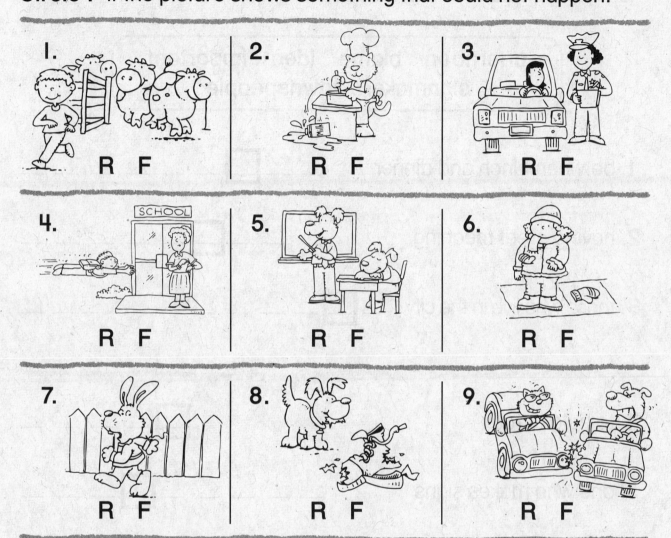

1. R   F
2. R   F
3. R   F
4. R   F
5. R   F
6. R   F
7. R   F
8. R   F
9. R   F

10. Draw a picture of a mistake that a real person might make.

Home Activity Your child looked at pictures to tell which events might happen in a realistic story and which might happen in a fantasy. Write a fantasy or realistic story together about one of the scenes pictured on this page. Have your child illustrate the story.

Practice Book Unit 5   **Comprehension** Realism and Fantasy   **95**

© Pearson Education 2

Name _____

Pick a word from the box to match each clue.
Write the letters of the word on the blanks.
The boxed letters spell two words.

> afternoon   blame   idea   important
> signmaker   townspeople

1. between lunch and dinner   _ _ ☐ _ _ _ _ _ _

2. having great meaning   _ _ _ ☐ _ _ _ _ _

3. those who live in the city   _ ☐ _ _ _ _ _ _ _ _ _

4. to hold at fault   ☐ _ _ _ _

5. one who makes signs   _ _ _ _ _ _ ☐ _ _

6. what you think up   _ _ ☐ _ _

What can you say if something goes wrong?
HINT: Find the words hidden in the boxes above.

_____   _____
-----------------------   -----------------------
_____   _____

Home Activity Your child used word clues to identify vocabulary words. Challenge your child to use some of this week's vocabulary words to make up a story about something that goes wrong. Work with your child to write the story. Then ask your child to read it aloud to you.

© Pearson Education 2

Name _____

Read the story.
Follow the directions.

The Rabbit and the Turtle
by Aesop

One day Rabbit and Turtle agreed to race. Soon Rabbit was far in front of Turtle. Rabbit was sure he would win, so he sat down to rest. Rabbit was soon asleep. Turtle kept on walking. In time he passed the sleeping Rabbit and won the race. When Rabbit woke up he got a big surprise!

---

1. **Circle** the author's name.

2. **Circle** the word below that tells what Rabbit and Turtle were doing.

   sleeping   racing   talking

3. **Circle** the part of the story that tells why Rabbit sat down.

4. **Underline** the part of the story that tells why Turtle won the race.

5. **Write** a sentence that tells why you think the author wrote this story.

_____

- -

_____

- -

Home Activity Your child answered questions about a fable and explained why the author wrote it. Read or tell a fairy tale or fable. Ask your child what he or she learned from the story. Discuss why authors sometimes use stories to teach important lessons.

© Pearson Education 2

Name _____

 **ph**one

 lau**gh**

Circle the word that has the same consonant sound heard at the end of lau**gh**.
Write the word on the line.

whale   dolphin

_____

1. We can use the _____ pitcher.

enough   much

_____

2. Did we make _____ ?

daughter   nephew

_____

3. Mr. Hill's _____ can help us.

trophy   medal

_____

4. We should get a _____ !

smile   laugh

_____

5. Don't _____. It's true.

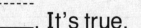

 Home Activity Your child reviewed words with the consonant sound /f/, spelled *ph* as in *phone* and *gh* as in *laugh*. Have your child write the lesson words on slips of paper. Take turns drawing words, spelling the words aloud, and using each word in a sentence.

© Pearson Education 2

Name _____

Pick a word from the box to finish the sentence.
Write the word on the line.

> afternoon   blame   idea   important
> signmaker   townspeople

_____
- -
1. An _____
   visitor was coming to town.

   _____
   -
2. All the _____ met together.

   _____
   -
3. They came up with an _____ .

   _____
   -
4. They told the _____ what to write.

   _____
   -
5. That _____ he held up his sign.

   _____
   -
6. No one could _____ him for it.

Home Activity Your child used lesson vocabulary to complete sentences. Ask your child to read each sentence to you. Challenge him or her to explain the meaning of the vocabulary words and use each word in a new sentence.

Practice Book Unit 5   **Lesson Vocabulary** **99**

© Pearson Education 2

Read Ana's Internet search results.
Write the answer to each question.

Search | painting |

1 <u>Painter's Supply</u>
   Paint, brushes, buckets. We sell **painting** supplies.

2 <u>100 Masters of **Painting**</u>
   Take an online tour. See some of the world's best **paintings**.

3 <u>Long Painters</u>
   No **painting** job too small—from one room to the entire house.

4 <u>Brush Up Your Paint Skills</u>
   Simple **painting** lessons that anyone can master.

---

1. What keyword did Ana enter? _____

2. Is <u>Painter's Supply</u> more likely to have a Web address that ends with **.com** or **.edu**? Explain.

_____

_____

3. At which Web site could Ana learn to paint?

_____

_____

4. How does <u>100 Masters of Painting</u> differ from <u>Long Painters</u>?

_____

_____

© Pearson Education 2

Home Activity Your child learned how to evaluate information from online sources. Ask your child to tell you about the different kinds of information available on the Internet. If possible, work with your child to gain access to the Internet and search for information on a topic of interest to your child.

Family Times

© Pearson Education 2

You are your child's first and best teacher!

Here are ways to help your child practice skills while having fun!

This week we're

Reading Just Like Josh Gibson

Just Like
**JOSH
GIBSON**

by Angela Johnson
illustrated by Beth Peck

Can a girl really hit a baseball just like Josh Gibson?

Talking About Why sports are important in our country

Learning About Contractions
Compare and Contrast

Day 1

Have your child read these words: *don't, I'd, they're, we'd, won't, you've.* Ask what two words make up each contraction.

Day 2

Your child has been making comparisons and contrasts. After reading a story together, discuss how the characters are alike and different.

Day 3

Have your child read these words: *bases, cheers, field, plate, sailed, threw.* Together, act out a sportscast using these words to describe a baseball game.

Day 4

Have your child write these spelling words: *can't, don't, he'd, I'd, I've, she'd, they'd, they're, we're, we've, won't, you're.* Then have your child write the words that make up the contractions and play a matching game.

Day 5

This week your child learned to use capital letters for the names of people, months, and cities. Have your child write and address a postcard, using capital letters where appropriate.

Memory Game

Materials index cards, pens or markers

Game Directions

1. Use index cards and pens or markers to make word cards as shown.

2. Mix up the cards and arrange them as shown face down.

3. Players take turns turning over a card and trying to match it. For instance, *you are* and *you're* would be a match.

4. If a match is found, player picks up the two matching cards. If there is no match, the cards are turned face down.

5. Play continues until all the cards are matched.

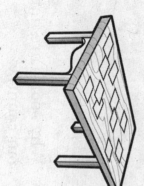

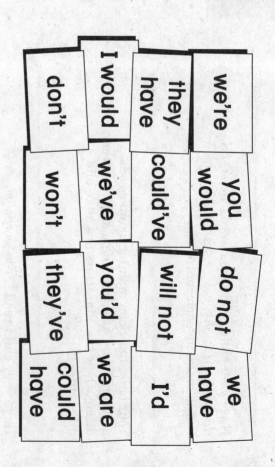

we're | you would
they have | you'd
I would | we've
don't | won't
they've | could have
do not | we have
will not | I'd
could've | we are

© Pearson Education 2

Name _____

Pick the contraction that is formed
from each pair of words.
Write the contraction on the line.

<u>You are</u> cute.
<u>You're</u> cute.

| can't | don't | I'd | I've | she'd |
| they'd | they're | we're | we've | won't |

1. we + have

_____
- - - - - - - - - - - - -
_____

2. I + would

_____
- - - - - - - - - - - - -
_____

3. will + not

_____
- - - - - - - - - - - - -
_____

4. they + are

_____
- - - - - - - - - - - - -
_____

5. I + have

_____
- - - - - - - - - - - - -
_____

6. can + not

_____
- - - - - - - - - - - - -
_____

7. we + are

_____
- - - - - - - - - - - - -
_____

8. they + would

_____
- - - - - - - - - - - - -
_____

9. do + not

_____
- - - - - - - - - - - - -
_____

10. she + would

_____
- - - - - - - - - - - - -
_____

© Pearson Education 2

Home Activity Your child wrote contractions with *'re (we're)*, *'ve (I've)*, *'d (I'd)*, and *'t (won't)*. Work with your child to make a set of flashcards with a word pair (such as *we are*) on one side and the matching contraction (such as *we're*) on the other. Help your child practice contractions using the flashcards.

Phonics Contractions **103**

Name _____

Read the story.
Follow the directions.

Rita and Will both love to play sports, but they do not like the same ones. Rita plays soccer. She enjoys the game because she likes to run. Will likes baseball. Unlike Rita, Will doesn't like to run much. He likes to hit the ball.

I. **Underline** the part of the story that tells how Rita and Will are alike.

2. **Write** the name of the person who likes soccer.

_____
- - - - - - - - - - - - - - - - -

3. **Write** the name of the person who likes baseball.

_____
- - - - - - - - - - - - - - - - -

4. **Write** a sentence to compare and contrast how Rita and Will feel about running.

_____
- -
_____
- -
_____

Use what you know about sports. **Think** about what you read. **List** another sport that Rita and Will might like.

_____
- -

5. Rita _____
- -
_____

6. Will _____

Home Activity Your child read a story and answered questions to compare and contrast two characters and their favorite sports. Ask your child to think about two games or activities he or she enjoys. Discuss what your child likes about them. Ask your child to tell how the activities are alike and different.

© Pearson Education 2

Name _____

field hockey

ice hockey

Look for ways in which ice hockey is like field hockey.
List one way they are **alike**.

1. _____
_____
_____

Look for ways in which ice hockey is **not** like field hockey.
List two ways they are **different**.

2. _____
_____
_____

3. _____
_____
_____

Home Activity Your child described ways in which two sports are alike and different. Use magazines, the newspaper, or the Internet to locate pictures of two other sports, such as soccer and football. Ask your child to name similarities and differences between the two sports.

© Pearson Education 2

Name _____

Pick a word from the box to match each clue.
Write the word on the line.

bases   cheers   field   plate   sailed   threw

1.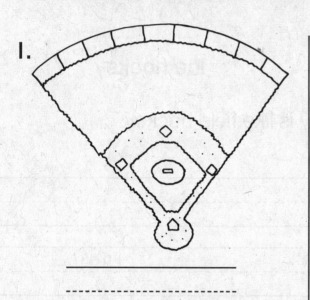

_____

- - - - - - - - - - -

_____

2.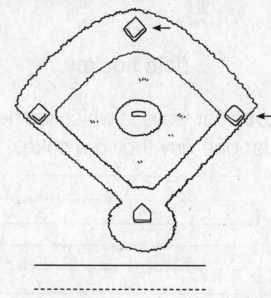

_____

- - - - - - - - - - -

_____

3. soared

_____

- - - - - - - - - - -

_____

4. tossed

_____

- - - - - - - - - - -

_____

5. yells and claps at a game

_____

- - - - - - - - - - -

_____

6. home base

_____

- - - - - - - - - - -

_____

Home Activity Your child used clues to identify and write words that he or she learned to read this week. Work with your child to write about an experience watching or playing baseball. Use as many of the vocabulary words as possible. Encourage your child to illustrate the writing.

© Pearson Education 2

Name _____

Write F before each statement of **fact**.
Write O before each statement of **opinion**.

_____

_____ 1. The first game of basketball was played in 1891.

_____ 2. Basketball is more fun than football.

_____ 3. More people pay to see basketball than any other sport.

_____ 4. Teams pay basketball players too much money.

5. **Write** a statement of **opinion** about basketball.

_____

_____

_____

_____

© Pearson Education 2

Home Activity Your child identified statements of fact and opinion about basketball. Discuss another sport with your child. Ask him or her to make two statements of fact about the sport. Then ask him or her to make two statements of opinion.

Name _____

saw    <u>au</u>to    c<u>augh</u>t    ch<u>al</u>k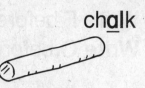

Circle the word for each picture. **Write** the word on the line.

1.

talk   took

_____

2.

hook   hawk

_____

3.

lawn   lane

_____

4.

small   smell

_____

5.

face   faucet

_____

6. 10 + 6 = 16

tote   taught

_____

Pick a word from the box to finish each sentence.
Write the word on the line.

> daughter   launch

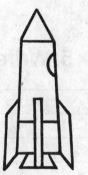

7. Anna and her _____ are late.

8. They will miss the _____.

© Pearson Education 2

 School + Home

Home Activity Your child reviewed words with the vowel sound in *fall,* spelled *aw* as in *saw, au* as in *auto, augh* as in *caught,* and *al* as in *chalk.* Ask your child to name words that rhyme with some of the lesson words above. Help your child write humorous sentences using pairs of rhyming words.

Name _____

Pick a word from the box to finish each sentence.
Write the word on the line.

> bases   cheers   field   plate   sailed   threw

1. Glenn looked at the players on the _____ .

2. He stepped up to the _____ and waited for the pitch.

3. The pitcher _____ the ball.

4. Glenn swung, and the ball _____ to left field.

5. He raced around the _____ .

6. He could hear the _____ of the fans.

Home Activity Your child used lesson vocabulary words to complete sentences. Ask your child to use the words to write a poem or song about baseball. Help your child write his or her ideas. Encourage your child to perform the piece for other family members.

© Pearson Education 2

Name _____

 coach
 Liz's grandma

Liz is doing a report about girls' baseball. **Look** at the pictures.
Write the answer to each item below.

1. Who could Liz talk to if she wants to find out about girls'

   _____

   -

   baseball today? _____

2. Write one good question Liz could ask to find out about girls'
   baseball today.

   _____

   -

   _____

3. Who could Liz talk to if she wants to find out about girls'

   _____

   -

   baseball long ago? _____

4. Write one good question Liz could ask to find out about girls'
   baseball long ago.

   _____

   -

   _____

5. Who could Liz talk to if she needs help finding books to use for

   _____

   -

   her report? _____

 Home Activity Your child learned about using people as resources for information. Talk with your child about the people you turn to when you need answers. Ask your child to write two questions to someone in your family or community.

© Pearson Education 2

Name

Family Times

You are your child's first and best teacher!

This week we're

Reading Red, White, and Blue: The Story of the American Flag

Talking About What our flag means

Learning About Inflected Endings
Fact and Opinion

© Pearson Education 2

Here are ways to help your child practice skills while having fun!

Day 1

Have your child read these words: *likes, tries, tried, trying, bigger, biggest.* Help your child check a newspaper or book to find words with the endings *-s, -es, -ed, -ing, -er,* or *-est.*

Day 2

Read aloud a letter, postcard, or other description of a place. Discuss which statements are facts and which are opinions.

Day 3

Have your child read these words: *America, birthday, flag, freedom, nicknames, stars, stripes.* Use the words to talk about ways people celebrate the Fourth of July.

Day 4

Have your child write these spelling words: *cried, crying, hiked, hiking, liked, liking, planned, planning, skipped, skipping, tried, trying.* Say a simple sentence using *cried* and *crying.* Ask your child to write it. Continue with other word pairs.

Day 5

This week your child used maps to aid understanding of a reading passage. Have your child write a story about a treasure map and together draw the map.

Sorting Fact From Opinion

Materials index cards, markers

Game Directions

1. Make a set of statement cards about the U. S. flag as shown.

2. Mix the cards and place them face down in a stack.

3. Players take turns drawing a card, reading it, and telling whether it is a statement of fact or opinion. If correct, player keeps the card.

4. Play continues until all the cards from the stack have been used.

Our flag has many nicknames.

The flag is so beautiful.

Old Glory is an odd name for a flag.

Flag Day is June 14.

The flag is red, white, and blue.

Everyone should have a flag.

The flag has white stars.

Flags can be big or small.

The flag needs more stripes.

Big flags look better than tiny ones.

Each star stands for one state.

Most countries have a flag.

© Pearson Education 2

Name _____

Read each word.
Find the base word.
Write the base word on the line.

try + -ed = tr**ied**   try + -ing = try**ing**

1. hiked _____   2. skipped _____

3. planning _____   4. shopping _____

5. cried _____   6. liking _____

7. baking _____   8. moved _____

Find the word that makes sense in the sentences below.
Mark the space to show your answer.

9. Sam _____ to help.
  ◯ beg
  ◯ begged
  ◯ begging

10. He likes _____.
  ◯ rake
  ◯ raked
  ◯ raking

Home Activity Your child identified base words with -*ed* and -*ing* endings, as in *tried* and *trying*. Read with your child, looking for words with -*ed* and -*ing* endings. Have your child pronounce the words and identify the base words.

© Pearson Education 2

Read the passage.
Follow the directions.

   Everyone should fly the flag. It even flies at the moon. People placed the flag there during the first moon landing. Many schools fly the flag. Helping to raise the school flag is the greatest thrill a student can have.

1. **Underline two** statements of **opinion** in the passage.

2. **Circle three** statements of **fact** in the passage.

3. **Think** about what you know. **Write one** statement of **fact** about the flag.

_____

- -

_____

- -

_____

4. **Think** about how you feel. **Write one** statement of **opinion** about the flag.

_____

- -

_____

- -

_____

© Pearson Education 2

Home Activity Your child read a passage about the U.S. flag and identified statements of fact and opinion. Talk with your child about the flag or other important national symbols. Work together to write one statement of fact and one statement of opinion about the topic you discussed.

Name _____

Write F before each
statement of **fact**.
Write O before each
statement of **opinion**.

_____
I. _____ Everyone should see Lady Liberty.

_____
2. _____ Lady Liberty shows a woman holding a torch.

_____
3. _____ She was a gift from the people of France.

_____
4. _____ The stairs inside are the best thing about it.

5. **Write** a statement of **opinion** about Lady Liberty.

_____

_____

_____

_____

Home Activity Your child identified statements of fact and opinion about the Statue of Liberty. With your child, think of an interesting monument or site in your city or neighborhood. Work together to write two statements of fact and two statements of opinion about your chosen subject.

© Pearson Education 2

Name _____

Pick a word from the box to match each clue.
Write the word. The **circled letters** spell two words.

America	birthday	flag
freedom	nicknames	stars	stripes

1. lights twinkling in the night sky

2. the day something is born

3. what people in this country enjoy

4. our country's is red, white, and blue

5. bands of color

6. United States of _____

7. what friends might call each other

8. Write the two words spelled by the circled letters.

_____   _____

- - - - - - - - - - - - - - - -   - - - - - - - - - - - - - - - -

_____   _____

Home Activity Your child used clues to solve puzzles using vocabulary words. Think of two other words that relate to the history and symbols of the United States. Work with your child to make puzzles for these two words. Then help your child write sentences using your new words and the words on this page.

© Pearson Education 2

Name _____

Read the text.
Follow the directions.

Where can you see our country's flag? You can see it on flagpoles. You can see it in parades. Many people wear flag pins. Some firefighters wear flag patches on their shirts. People feel proud of our flag.

1. **Circle** the answer below that tells what the text is all about.

   the flag   parades   firefighters

2. **Circle** the answer below that tells the main idea.

   People fly the flag from flagpoles.

   People carry the flag in parades.

   People are proud of our flag.

3. **Draw** a picture to show a detail about the main idea.

Home Activity Your child identified the main idea and details in a paragraph about the U.S. flag. Read a story or nonfiction selection about this country or its people. Stop to talk about the most important ideas in the passage. Ask your child to draw a picture to show a detail from the reading.

Practice Book Unit 6   **Comprehension** Main Idea Review **117**

© Pearson Education 2

Name _____

Write the contraction on the line.

You are cute.
You're cute.

1. they would

_____
- - - - - - - - - - - -
_____

2. we have

_____
- - - - - - - - - - - -
_____

3. you are

_____
- - - - - - - - - - - -
_____

4. do not

_____
- - - - - - - - - - - -
_____

5. he would

_____
- - - - - - - - - - - -
_____

6. we are

_____
- - - - - - - - - - - -
_____

7. will not

_____
- - - - - - - - - - - -
_____

8. can not

_____
- - - - - - - - - - - -
_____

Find the contraction for each pair of words.
Mark the space to show your answer.

9. they are
   - ⬭ there
   - ⬭ they're
   - ⬭ they've

10. I have
   - ⬭ I'd
   - ⬭ I'm
   - ⬭ I've

© Pearson Education 2

Home Activity Your child reviewed contractions with *'re (we're)*, *'ve (I've)*, *'d (I'd)*, and *n't (won't)*. Work with your child to write sentences using the contractions on this page. Then have your child circle each contraction and tell what pair of words the contraction represents.

Name _____

Pick a word from the box to finish each sentence.
Write the word on the line.

America	birthday	flag	freedom
nicknames	stars	stripes	

1. July 4, 1776, is the _____ of this country.

2. Many people fly the _____ on July 4.

3. Our flag has 13 _____.

4. It has 50 _____.

5. People have many _____ for the flag.

6. No matter what we call it, the flag reminds us of our _____ _____.

7. It stands for our country, the United States of _____.

Home Activity Your child used lesson vocabulary words to complete sentences. Work with your child to write a paragraph describing what he or she most appreciates about this country. Try to include as many vocabulary words as possible.

© Pearson Education 2

Read the paragraph. **Fill** in the notes below.

How to Fly the Flag

We have many customs that tell how to fly our country's flag. The flag should be put up each morning and taken down each night. Some fly the flag 24 hours a day. When they do, a light should shine on the flag at night. The flag should not fly in bad weather unless a special flag is used. When the flag hangs on the same pole as a state or city flag, it should be the highest. These customs help people show respect for the flag.

_____

1. up in morning, down _____

_____

2. if up 24 hours, _____

3. if bad weather,

_____

_____

4. if with state or city flag,

_____

_____

5. flag customs show

_____

_____

© Pearson Education 2

Home Activity Your child practiced taking notes about a reading passage. Ask your child to read a paragraph from a textbook or other nonfiction book. Talk about the most important information. Have your child use his or her own words to make brief notes about the reading.

Family Times

You are your child's first and best teacher!

This week we're

Reading A Birthday Basket for Tía

Talking About Why family celebrations are special

Learning About Syllables -tion, -ture
Drawing Conclusions

© Pearson Education 2

Here are ways to help your child practice skills while having fun!

Day 1

Have your child read these words: *caution, pasture, nation, nature.* Ask what sound is heard in the second syllable of each word.

Day 2

Your child has been learning to draw conclusions. After reading a story, discuss whether the characters' actions make sense.

Day 3

Have your child read these words: *aunt, bank, basket, collects, feature, fixture, future, favorite, present.* Take turns giving clues and guessing the words.

Day 4

Have your child write these spelling words: *action, caution, feature, fixture, future, mixture, motion, nation, nature, picture, section, station.* Help your child think of ways to use each word to make a sign, such as *use caution.*

Day 5

This week your child has been discussing customs and writing summaries. Have your child write a summary of ways your family celebrates birthdays or other special days. Help your child find photos or draw pictures of these celebrations.

Finish the Word

Materials coin, buttons

Game Directions

1. Players take turns flipping a coin and moving their buttons one space for heads or two spaces for tails.

2. Players add *tion* or *ture* to the letters in each space on the game board to finish the words. A player then uses the word in a sentence. If a player cannot finish the word and use it correctly in a sentence, the player moves back to the previous position.

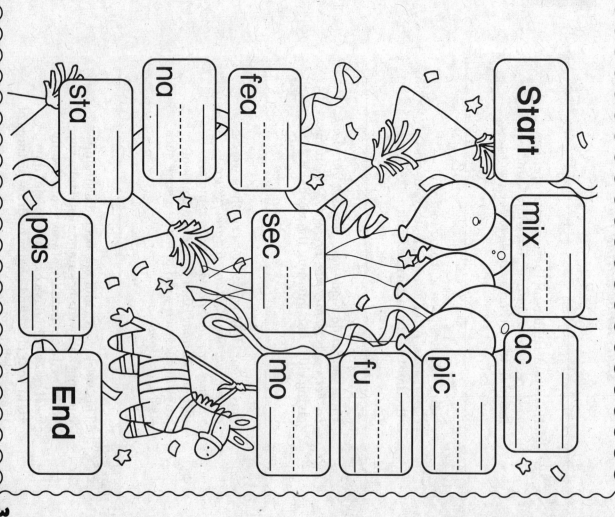

Start

mix ____

ac ____

pic ____

fu ____

mo ____

sec ____

fea ____

na ____

sta ____

pas ____

End

© Pearson Education 2

Name _____

Circle a word with **-tion** or **-ture**
to finish each sentence.

na**tion**   mix**ture**

1. I saw a horse in the _____ .

portion
pasture

2. I watched from one _____ of the yard.

section
suction

3. I moved with _____ .

culture
caution

4. I walked in slow _____ .

motion
notion

5. Then I took a _____ .

mixture
picture

© Pearson Education 2

School + Home

Home Activity Your child wrote words that include the syllables -*tion* as in *nation* and -*ture* as in *mixture*.
Write some other words with -*tion* or -*ture*, such as *future, nature, texture, action,* and *station.* Have your
child read each word and identify the final syllable pattern.

Name _____

Read the story. **Look** at the picture. **Follow** the directions.

   The children were laughing and having fun. A paper piñata hung above them. One at a time, each child took a turn to swing. Finally, the piñata broke open. Candy and small toys fell to the ground. Everyone ran to grab a handful.

―――――――――――――――――――――――――――

Circle the word that best finishes each sentence.
Write the word on the line.

happy   sad
_____

1. The children were _____.

game   sport
_____

2. They were playing a _____.

meeting   party
_____

3. They were at a _____.

―――――――――――――――――――――――――――

4. **Write** a sentence to tell why the children swung at the piñata.

_____

_____

_____

Home Activity Your child read a passage and drew conclusions from the passage and its illustration. Read your child a favorite book. As you read, pause to discuss what is happening. Ask your child open-ended questions, such as "What's going on now?" and "What's this all about?"

© Pearson Education 2

Name _____

Read the story. **Ask** yourself **what is happening.**
Answer each question.

Miss Booker stood by her door.
She heard whispers inside. As she
entered, the children yelled. For
a minute Miss Booker didn't know
what was going on. Then she looked
around. Everyone was smiling and
had on silly hats. They had even
made a sign for this happy day.

_____

- -

1. Who is Miss Booker? _____

_____

- -

2. Where is she? _____

3. Why didn't she know what was going on?

_____

- -

_____

4. Draw a picture of the sign the children made.

© Pearson Education 2

School + Home

Home Activity Your child read a story and drew conclusions from the information in the story and
illustration. Take turns reading another story with your child. Work together to figure out more about the
characters and what happens in the story as you read.

Practice Book Unit 6   **Comprehension** Draw Conclusions   **125**

Name _____

Pick a word from the box to match each clue.
Write the word on the line.

> aunt   bank   basket
> collects   favorite   present

1.

_____
_____

2.

_____
_____

3. a place where people keep money

_____
_____

4. the one you like best

_____
_____

5. Your mother's sister is your
_____.

_____
_____

6. saves

_____
_____

Home Activity Your child used clues to identify and write vocabulary words learned this week. Ask your child to describe his or her dream birthday. Help your child write a description of the day. Encourage your child to use lesson vocabulary words in the writing.

© Pearson Education 2

Name _____

Read each sentence.
Answer the questions.

1. Viv was late, so she missed the party.
   Why did Viv miss the party?

   _____

   _____

2. Because Jim forgot, he did not send a birthday card.
   Why didn't Jim send a birthday card?

   _____

   _____

3. Mom burned the cake, so no one could eat it.
   Why couldn't anyone eat the cake?

   _____

   _____

4. Because Al dropped the box, the gift broke.
   Why did the gift break?

   _____

   _____

5. Tim was sad because so many things went wrong.
   Why was Tim sad?

   _____

   _____

Home Activity Your child read sentences to see what happened and answered questions about the cause of each event. Talk to your child about events of the day. Ask your child what happened and why. Have him or her draw a picture to show one thing that happened and write a sentence to tell why it happened.

© Pearson Education 2

Name _____

Add the ending to each word.
Write the new word on the line.

try + -ed = tr**ied**
try + -ing = try**ing**
reach + -es = reach**es**

1. race + es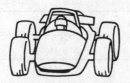

_____

- - - - - - - - - -

2. chase + es

_____

- - - - - - - - - -

3. cry + ed

_____

- - - - - - - - - -

4. smile + ing

_____

- - - - - - - - - -

5. skip + ing

_____

- - - - - - - - - -

6. plan + ed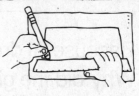

_____

- - - - - - - - - -

7. hop + ing

_____

- - - - - - - - - -

8. bake + ed

_____

- - - - - - - - - -

School + Home   **Home Activity** Your child reviewed and wrote words with *-ed*, *-ing, and -es* endings, as in *tried*, *trying*, and *reaches*. Work with your child to write a story using some of the words on this page. Have your child circle each word with an *-ed*, *-ing*, or *-es* ending and name the base word.

© Pearson Education 2

Name _____

Pick a word from the box to finish each sentence.
Write the word on the line.

aunt	bank	basket
collects	favorite	present

_____

----

1. Matt's _____ came to visit on his birthday.

_____

----

2. Matt's aunt _____ coins.

3. This year she got some pennies from

_____

----

the _____.

_____

----

4. She filled a _____ with the money.

5. Then she gave it to Matt as a

_____

----

birthday _____.

_____

----

6. It was Matt's _____.

School + Home

Home Activity Your child used lesson vocabulary words to complete sentences. Ask your child to use each word in another sentence. Help your child write the sentences. Have your child draw a picture to illustrate each sentence.

© Pearson Education 2

Name _____

Read the Internet online directory. **Answer** each question.

File   Edit   View   Favorites   Tools   Help

http://www.url.here

Home and Family
Parenting, Kids, Family Life

The Arts
Drawing, Painting, Artists

Music and Movies
Rock, Country, Pop, Movies,
Movie Stars

Sports and Games
Team Sports, Sports Heroes,
Board Games, Online Games

1. **Write** the **main topic** where you'll find craft ideas.

_____

_____

2. **Write** the **main topic** where you'll find songs.

_____

_____

3. **Write** the **main topic** to find party games.

_____

_____

4. **Write** the **main topic** where parents will find tips for raising children.

_____

_____

Home Activity Your child learned how to use an online directory to find information. Ask your child to explain the difference between an online directory and a search engine and tell the advantages of each. If practical, access an online directory together to search for information.

© Pearson Education 2

Name

Family Times

You are your child's first and best teacher!

This week we're

Reading Cowboys

What was it like to live as a cowboy?

COWBOYS

by Lucille Recht Penner
illustrated by Ben Carter

Genre Nonfiction gives information about real people, places, and events.

Talking About Why we should learn
about cowboys

Learning About Suffixes -ness, -less
Cause and Effect

© Pearson Education 2

*Here are ways to help your child practice
skills while having fun!*

 Day 1

Have your child read these words: *darkness,
endless, goodness, useless.* Help your child
make a list of other words that end with the
suffixes -*ness* or -*less.*

 Day 2

Your child has been discussing cause and
effect. As you read together, discuss events
and their causes.

 Day 3

Have your child read these words: *campfire,
cattle, cowboy, galloped, herd, railroad, trails.*
Together, make picture cards for each word.

 Day 4

Have your child write these spelling words:
*careless, darkness, fearless, fitness, goodness,
helpless, kindness, sadness, sickness,
thankless, useless, weakness.* Take turns giving
clues, guessing, and spelling each word.

 Day 5

This week your child has been learning
to write a research report. Help your child
find out more about cowboys and write
a paragraph summarizing what he or
she learned.

Cause-and-Effect Match-Up

Materials index cards, crayons or markers

Game Directions

1. Make a set of picture cards as shown. Mix the cards and spread them face down on a table or the floor.

2. Players take turns turning over two cards at a time, trying to match up the cause card with the effect card.

3. Players keep matching pairs. If a match is not made, players return cards to their original positions.

4. Play until all matches are made.

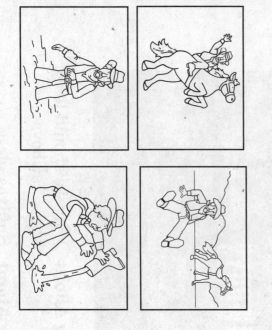

© Pearson Education 2

Name _____

Add -ness or **-less** to each word
to make a word from the box.
Write the new word on the line.

 sad**ness**

 care**less**

darkness	endless	fearless	fitness
goodness	kindness	useless	thankless

1. good

_____

_____

2. use

_____

_____

3. thank

_____

_____

4. fit

_____

_____

5. kind

_____

_____

6. end

_____

_____

Pick a word from the box to match each clue.
Write the word on the line.

_____

7. brave _____

_____

8. without light _____

 School + Home **Home Activity** Your child wrote words with the suffixes *-ness* as in *sadness* and *-less* as in *careless*. Help your child write other words with these suffixes, such as *helpless, painless, sickness,* and *weakness.* Ask your child to read each word and identify the base word (such as *help* in *helpless*).

© Pearson Education 2

Name _____

Look at each picture.
Answer the questions.

1. **Why** did the horse go up on two legs?

_____

- -

_____

2. **Why** did the fire go out?

_____

- -

_____

3. **Why** did the wagon stop moving?

_____

- -

_____

4. **Why** did the cowboy's hat come off?

_____

- -

_____

© Pearson Education 2

Home Activity Your child looked at pictures to see what happened and answered questions about the cause of each event. With your child, look at pictures in a book or magazine. Discuss what is going on in the pictures. Ask your child to tell why these things happened.

Name _____

Read each sentence.
Answer the questions.

1. The family wanted new land,
   so they moved West.
   Why did the family move West?

_____
- -
_____

2. Because the hills were steep, the ox got tired.
   Why did the ox get tired?

_____
- -
_____

3. They came to a pond, so they stopped for water.
   Why did they stop for water?

_____
- -
_____

4. The trail turned to mud because of the rain.
   Why did the trail turn to mud?

_____
- -
_____

5. The wagon got stuck in the mud.
   Why did the wagon get stuck?

_____
- -
_____

Home Activity Your child answered questions about why things happened. Work with your child to write a story about a trip or drive you have taken together. As you plan your story, discuss what happened and why these things happened. Encourage your child to add an illustrated cover to the story.

© Pearson Education 2

Practice Book Unit 6   **Comprehension** Cause and Effect   **135**

Name _____

Pick a word from the box to match each clue.
Write the word in the puzzles. The **circled letters** spell two words.

> campfire   cattle   cowboy
> galloped   herd   railroad   trails

1. how a horse ran

2. tracks and trains

3. a group of cows

4. he takes care of cattle

5. an outdoor fire

6. paths

7. cows or bulls

1. ☐☐☐◯☐☐☐☐

2. ☐☐☐◯☐☐☐☐

3. ☐☐☐◯

4. ☐☐◯☐☐☐

5. ☐☐☐☐☐☐◯

6. ☐☐☐☐◯

7. ☐☐☐◯☐☐

8. Write the two words spelled by the circled letters.

_____   _____

------------------   ------------------

 Home Activity Your child used clues to solve puzzles, using vocabulary words. Ask your child to use the lesson vocabulary words to write a tall tale (a story that uses exaggeration) about a cowboy. Suggest that your child draw a picture to show what the main character looks like.

© Pearson Education 2

Name _____

Write F before each statement of **fact.**
Write O before each statement of **opinion.**

1. _____ Many people went West by wagon train.

2. _____ They wanted new land for farms and ranches.

3. _____ The worst part of the trip was saying good-bye to family and friends.

4. _____ Many people turned back before they got to the West.

5. **Write** a statement of **opinion** about the West.

_____

_____

_____

© Pearson Education 2

Home Activity Your child identified statements of fact and opinion about the settling of the American West. Ask your child what else he or she has been learning about the West. Work together to write two statements of fact and two statements of opinion about that period in American history.

Practice Book Unit 6   **Comprehension** Fact and Opinion Review   **137**

Name _____

Circle the word for each picture.
Write the word on the line.

na**tion** mix**ture**

1.

lotion   letter

_____

- - - - - - - - - - - - - - -

2.

printer   picture

_____

- - - - - - - - - - - - - - -

3.

member   motion

_____

- - - - - - - - - - - - - - -

4.

silver   section

_____

- - - - - - - - - - - - - - -

5.

capture   circus

_____

- - - - - - - - - - - - - - -

6.

street   station

_____

- - - - - - - - - - - - - - -

Find the word that has the same final syllable as the picture.
Mark the space to show your answer.

7. ⬭ father
⬭ feature
⬭ fallen

8. ⬭ caution
⬭ creature
⬭ cartoon

© Pearson Education 2

 School + Home **Home Activity** Your child reviewed and wrote words with the final syllable pattern *-tion* as in *nation*, and *-ture* as in *mixture*. Work with your child to write a poem or story using words from this page. Encourage your child to illustrate his or her work and then share it with friends or family.

Name _____

Pick a word from the box to finish each sentence.
Write the word on the line.

campfire	cattle
cowboy	galloped
herd	railroad	trails

1. Tanya read a book about a _____ who lived long ago.

2. He moved the _____ of cattle to market.

3. Sometimes storms scared the _____ .

4. The cowboy and his horse _____ after them.

5. Then the cowboy built a _____ and went to sleep.

6. He led the cattle down dusty _____ .

7. Then the _____ took the cattle to the East.

© Pearson Education 2

Home Activity Your child used lesson vocabulary words to complete sentences. Have your child use the vocabulary words to tell another story. Help your child record the story. Ask your child to read the story and underline each vocabulary word.

Name _____

Read the synonyms for **good** and **wet**. **Answer** each question.

good I expert, skilled; **2** caring, honest; **3** healthful, tasty
wet damp, soaked, soggy, sopping, flooded

1. Which words could you use instead of *good* in this sentence?
   The cook fixed the cowboys a good dinner.

   _____

   -

   _____

2. Which words could you use instead of *good* in this sentence?
   The cowboy was a good person.

   _____

   -

   _____

3. Which words could you use instead of *good* in this sentence?
   The cowboy was a good rider and never fell off his horse.

   _____

   -

   _____

4. Which words could you use instead of *wet* in this sentence?
   After three days of rain, the cattle trail was wet.

   _____

   -

   _____

5. Why would a thesaurus be helpful when writing?

   _____

   -

   _____

© Pearson Education 2

Home Activity Your child learned how to use a thesaurus to find synonyms, or words with similar meanings. Think of a common word, such as *say*. Help your child brainstorm other words that could be used in place of *say*, such as *speak, answer, reply, state, cry,* or *declare.*

Name

Family Times

You are your child's first and best teacher!

This week we're

Reading Jingle Dancer

Talking About How different people celebrate

Learning About Prefixes *mis-, mid-*
Character, Setting, Plot

© Pearson Education 2

Here are ways to help your child practice skills while having fun!

Day 1

Have your child read these words: *midday, midweek, misprint, misspell*. Ask your child to name each base word and tell how the prefix *mid-* or *mis-* changes its meaning.

Day 2

Your child has been discussing character, setting, and plot. After reading a story together, ask how the characters changed by the end of the story.

Day 3

Have your child read these words: *borrow, clattering, drum, jingles, silver, voice*. Together, make up a song that uses these words.

Day 4

Have your child write these spelling words: *midair, midday, midway, midweek midyear, misbehave, misdeed, mislead, mismatch, misplace, misprint, mistake*. Take turns using these words in a silly story about a very bad day.

Day 5

This week your child has been learning to write with words that appeal to the senses. Have your child write a description of a celebration or special event. Tell your child to choose words that vividly describe sights, sounds, and smells.

Add a Prefix

Materials white paper, scissors, pencil, paper clip, buttons

Game Directions

1. Make a simple spinner as shown.
2. Two players each place a button on a **Start** space. Players take turns spinning to get a prefix.
3. If the prefix on the spinner can be combined with the word on the next game board space to make a word, the player says the new word and moves the button to that space.
4. Play continues until both players reach the "End" box.

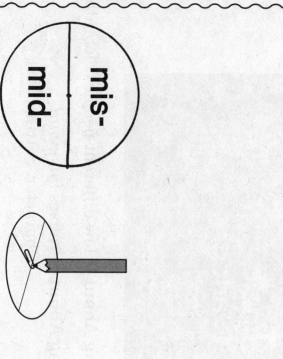

mis-

mid-

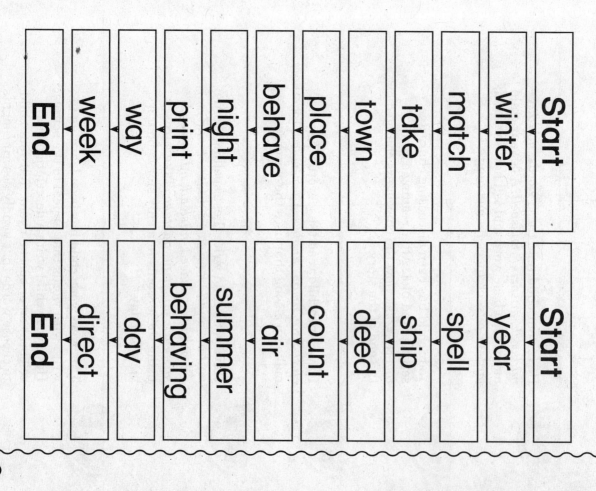

© Pearson Education 2

Start	Start
winter	year
match	spell
take	ship
town	deed
place	count
behave	air
night	summer
print	behaving
way	day
week	direct
End	End

Name _____

Read the clues.
Write mid or **mis**
to finish the word.

 <u>mid</u>air   <u>mis</u>place

---

1. middle of the week

_____

_____ week

2. an error

_____

_____ take

3. act badly

_____

_____ behave

4. noon

_____

_____ day

5. about July 1

_____

_____ year

6. an error in printing

_____

_____ print

7. a wrong act

_____

_____ deed

8. middle of winter

_____

_____ winter

9. make a spelling error

_____

_____ spell

10. middle of the ship

_____

_____ ship

Home Activity Your child wrote words with the prefixes *mid-* (as in *midair*) and *mis-* (as in *misplace*).
Together, name other words with the prefixes *mid-* and *mis-*, such as *midway, midsize, mislead, misfile,* and
misdirect. Write the words. Ask your child to pronounce them and identify the prefixes.

© Pearson Education 2

Name _____

Read the story. **Follow** the directions.

Anna was excited to be visiting the small village where her grandparents lived. It was Saturday night, and the villagers were having a dance. Anna's grandmother had showed her the steps. As the band began to play, Anna hummed. Then her grandfather took her hand, and they began to spin!

1. **Underline** the part of the story that tells where the story takes place.

2. **Circle** the words that tell when the story takes place.

3. **Underline** the word that tells how Anna feels.

4. **Write** a sentence to tell what Anna does when she hears the music.

_____

- -

_____

5. **Draw** a picture of what happens at the end of the story.

© Pearson Education 2

Home Activity Your child read a story and answered questions about its characters, setting, and plot. Work with your child to write a story about a celebration or holiday. Before you begin, talk about who will be in the story, where and when it will take place, and what will happen.

Name _____

Read the story. **Answer** the questions.

Ved peeked into the living room. It was filled with friends and family. Everyone had come for the feast. Ved felt left out. No one even knew he was there. Then his mother called to him. Ved flew into her arms. A smile filled his face.

1. Where did the story take place?

_____

- -

_____

2. At first, how did Ved feel about the party?

_____

- -

_____

3. Underline the sentence that tells what Ved's mother did.

4. Circle the sentence that tells what Ved did then.

5. Draw a picture that shows how Ved felt at the end of the story.

© Pearson Education 2

 Home Activity Your child read a story and answered questions about its characters, setting, and plot. Read a favorite story with your child. Ask your child to tell where and when it takes place. Then discuss how the characters affect what happens in the story.

Name _____

Pick a word from the box to match each clue.
Write the word on the line.

> borrow   clattering   drum
> jingles   silver   voice

1.

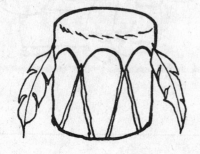

_____
- - - - - - - - - - - - - - - -
_____

2.

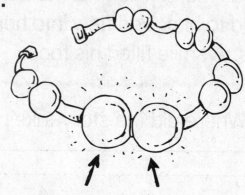

_____
- - - - - - - - - - - - - - - -
_____

3. opposite of **lend**

_____
- - - - - - - - - - - - - - - -
_____

4. rattling noise

_____
- - - - - - - - - - - - - - - -
_____

5. musical sounds like
   little bells

_____
- - - - - - - - - - - - - - - -
_____

6. what you hear when
   someone talks

_____
- - - - - - - - - - - - - - - -
_____

© Pearson Education 2

Home Activity Your child used clues to identify lesson vocabulary words. Ask your child to read the list of words. Work with your child to write sentences to describe the sounds he or she might hear at a celebration or party. Try to use as many vocabulary words as possible.

Name _____

Read each sentence.
Answer the questions.

1. Kiko planned a party because she wanted to do something with friends on New Year's Day. **Why** did Kiko plan a party?

_____

_____

_____

_____

2. Kiko called her friends so they would know what time to come to the party. **Why** did Kiko call her friends?

_____

_____

_____

_____

3. Because Kiko wanted the party to be fun, she got some games to play. **Why** did Kiko get games for the party?

_____

_____

_____

_____

Home Activity Your child read sentences about things that happened and wrote about why those things happened (cause and effect). Work with your child to write sentences about what people do to prepare for celebrations and why they do those things. Ask your child to illustrate the writing.

© Pearson Education 2

Name _____

Add -ness or **-less** to each word.
Write the new word on the line.

sad**ness**   care**less**

Add -ness	**Add -less**
1. sick _____	2. price _____
3. fit _____	4. pain _____
5. dark _____	6. spot _____
7. good _____	8. thank _____

Draw a picture of one animal that looks fearless and one that looks helpless.

9. fearless

10. helpless

© Pearson Education 2

School + Home **Home Activity** Your child reviewed and wrote words with the suffixes -ness as in sadness, and -less as in careless. Work with your child to write sentences using these words. Have your child read the words and underline the suffixes.

148 **Phonics** Suffixes -ness, -less Review   **Practice Book Unit 6**

Name _____

Pick a word from the box to finish each sentence.
Write the word on the line.

> borrow   clattering   drum
> jingles   silver   voice

1. The beat of the _____ is fast.

2. The dancer's dress _____ .

3. The sun makes the _____ pieces on the dress shine.

4. A rattle makes a _____ sound.

5. In a quiet _____, I speak to my friend.

6. "May I please _____ your camera?"

Home Activity Your child used lesson vocabulary words to complete sentences. Ask your child to tell you what he or she has been learning about jingle dancers. Together, write a paragraph to describe their traditions. Encourage your child to use lesson vocabulary words in the description.

© Pearson Education 2

Name _____

Mary made this time line about her life. **Use** the time line to answer the questions.

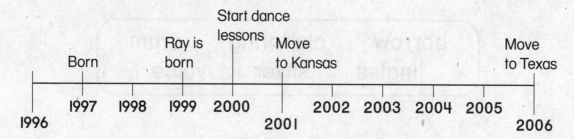

I. What are the first and last years marked on the time line?

_____   _____

- - - - - - - - - - - -   - - - - - - - - - - - -

_____   _____

_____

- - - - - - - - - - - -

2. When was Mary born? _____

_____

- - - - - - - - - - - -

3. When was Ray born? _____

4. What happened in 2006?

_____

- -

_____

- -

_____

_____

- - - - - - - - - - - -

5. How long did Mary live in Kansas? _____

Home Activity Your child learned how to read a time line. Have your child make a time line of his or her life or of the life of another family member. Help your child think of significant events and dates to place on the time line. Ask your child to explain the time line to others.

© Pearson Education 2

Name _____

Computer Keyboard

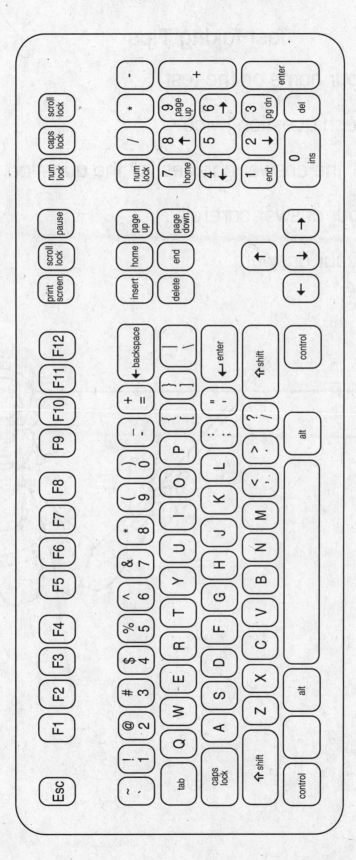

© Pearson Education 1

Test-Taking Tips

1. Write your name on the test.

2. Read each question twice.

3. Read all the answer choices for the question.

4. Mark your answer carefully.

5. Check your answer.

© Pearson Education 1

Name _____

© Pearson Education 1

Reading Log

Date	What is the title?	Who is the author?	What did you think of it?

Name _____

Date	What is the title?	Who is the author?	What did you think of it?

© Pearson Education 1

Practice Book

Name _____

Date	What is the title?	Who is the author?	What did you think of it?

© Pearson Education 1

Name _____

Date	What is the title?	Who is the author?	What did you think of it?

© Pearson Education 1

Practice Book